€8

E-ro:

The Basic

Whole-Hearted Healing™

Manual

(Third Edition)

Books from the Institute for the Study of Peak States Press

www.PeakStates.com

The Basic Whole-Hearted Healing™ Workbook (Volume 1), by Paula Courteau.

The Basic Whole-Hearted Healing™ Manual (Third Edition), by Grant McFetridge and Mary Pellicer MD.

Peak States of Consciousness: Theory and Applications, Volume 1: Breakthrough Techniques for Exceptional Quality of Life (2nd edition), by Grant McFetridge with Jacquelyn Aldana, Dr. James Hardt, and Alexandre Nadeau.

Peak States of Consciousness: Theory and Applications, Volume 2: Acquiring Extraordinary Spiritual and Shamanic States, by Grant McFetridge

Peak States of Consciousness: Theory and Applications, Volume 3: Applying Peak States to Research and Healing, by Grant McFetridge (forthcoming).

Silencing the Voices: From Mind-Chatter to Schizophrenia, by Grant McFetridge (forthcoming).

The Inner Peace Process, 2002. (A training video, 2 hours, VHS).

Institute for the Study of Peak States

The Basic

Whole-Hearted Healing™

Manual

(Third Edition)

by

Grant McFetridge

and

Mary Pellicer, M. D.

Third Edition

First printing, 2004

Library and Archives Canada Cataloguing in Publication

McFetridge, Grant, 1955-

    The basic whole-hearted healing manual / by Grant McFetridge and Mary Pellicer. -- 3rd ed.

    At head of title: Institute for the Study of Peak States.

Includes bibliographical references and index.

ISBN 0-9734680-2-5

    1. Regression (Psychology)--Therapeutic use. 2. Peak experiences.

I. Pellicer, Mary, 1955- II. Institute for the Study of Peak States III. Title.

RC489.R42M23 2004   615.8'51   C2004-904101-0

Institute for the Study of Peak States Press

3310 Cowie Road
Hornby Island, British Columbia
Canada
V0R 1Z0
http://www.peakstates.com

Legal Liability Agreement

IMPORTANT! READ THE FOLLOWING BEFORE CONTINUING THE TEXT!

The material in this book is provided for educational purposes only, and is **not** intended to be used by the general public as a self-help aid. The processes in this book are for the benefit of professionals in the field of trauma healing, and are not meant to be used by lay people without **competent and qualified supervision**. As this is a relatively new and specialized field of study, even most licensed professionals do not have adequate background and training in both prenatal and perinatal psychology and power therapies.

It is possible, and in some cases probable that you will feel extreme distress, both short and long term, if you use the processes in this book. As with any intense psychological process life-threatening problems might occur due to the possibility of stressing a weak heart, from activating suicidal feelings, and other causes. Although we've explicitly indicated in the text the potential problems that you might encounter using these processes, you may encounter something we haven't seen before. You may experience serious or life-threatening problems with any of the processes in this book. The possibility that you may die from using these processes **does** exist.

Given what we've just said, the following common sense statements constitute a legal agreement between us. This applies to everyone, including licensed professionals and lay people. Please read the following statements carefully:

1. I, any people associated with the Institute for the Study of Peak States, and the other authors in this text cannot and will not take responsibility for what you do with these techniques.

2. You are required to take complete responsibility for your own emotional and physical well being if you use these processes or any variations.

3. You are required to instruct others whom you use these processes on, or use variations of these processes on, that they are completely responsible for their own emotional and physical well-being.

4. Use these techniques under the supervision of a qualified therapist or physician as appropriate.

5. You must agree to hold harmless myself and anyone associated with this text or with the Institute for the Study of Peak States from any claims made by anyone who you use these or variations of these processes on, yourself included.

Continuing on in this text constitutes a legal agreement to these conditions. Thanks for your understanding.

Using This Manual For Self-Study

This manual is written for workshop students who are learning the process over a four day period. We've also make it available for interested lay people and other professionals who are interested in knowing the 'nuts and bolts' of basic Whole-Hearted Healing.

In a workshop setting, we can supervise and assist both during and after the workshop. If you intend to use this book for self-study, be aware that these processes are potentially dangerous. If you are not willing to be TOTALLY responsible for how you use this material, and any consequences to doing so, then we require that you not use the processes in this book. This should be obvious, but we wanted to make it totally explicit.

Acknowledgements

This book is dedicated to all of our workshop participants whose interest in learning this material, and courage in facing themselves in group settings was both a personal inspiration as well as our motivation for writing this manual.

I also want to acknowledge the following people who contributed to this manual and the material in it:

Ron Mied, who first pointed out the importance of the out-of-body images to trauma, and who worked with Grant while he slowly developed the WHH process;

Dr. Marie Green and Dr. Deola Perry whose personal and financial contributions made this work possible, and who created the first workshops for this material, helped refine it, and inspired us to continue working in this area;

The wonderful men and women who hosted our workshops over the years - especially Debra York, Patsy de Courey-Ireland, Meryl Beck, and Matt Fox;

Kate Sorensen who invited us to present our material at her power therapy conferences, which made such a big impact in our ability to share this material and the number of people who became aware of it;

Gary Craig, the developer of EFT who included our process on his links page which helped greatly in making it available to a wider audience;

And Dr. Mary Pellicer, co-author, co-teacher and colleague whose irrepressible good humor and skill made these workshops something to look forward to.

Table of Contents & Course Outline

Day 1

WHOLE-HEARTED HEALING TRAINING OVERVIEW

Welcome to the basic Whole-Hearted Healing training!

About the Institute for the Study of Peak States

The Institute puts on these trainings for two main reasons: 1) To give healers and people healing themselves another very powerful tool to heal with, and 2) To get a foundation tool in order to learn more advanced techniques, in order to work on the projects of the Institute. (Of course, some people will learn more advanced techniques and choose not to join the Institute, but for now that's the purpose of our advanced trainings.)

We at the Institute are using basic Whole-Hearted Healing and other processes to investigate fundamental questions and problems of humanity - what causes peak states of consciousness, how many of them are there, and how to acquire them; why are people unable to heal their bodies nearly instantly; what unusual abilities can people acquire, such as unusual vision states; and various clinical projects such as schizophrenia, autism, cancer, neuromuscular disease, and addictions.

We hope that after you take this class, you will contact us with any improvements that come up in your practice or personal work. We'll gladly put them on the website so that your colleagues can share your experience. Thanks!

How is basic Whole-Hearted Healing useful?

Basic WHH is one of a group of very effective and efficient therapies called 'power therapies'. At this time there are 6 of these different approaches to the problem of healing, (with quite a number of variations on these techniques). Like these other healing modalities, basic WHH is relatively fast - typically less than 1 hour per issue - and can be used for virtually anything that a client has discomfort with. We'll be going into particulars during the course of this training.

In the section of this class on other therapies, you'll see that we recommend learning some of the other power therapies first, because they can be easier and faster to use for the client (EFT and TAT are specific examples). WHH's advantage is in becoming able to understand why a particular problem occurred, and will often work when the other power therapies you know are not effective. Too, basic WHH can be used in conjunction with other power therapies, making them much more effective. To summarize, like any therapy some clients will respond well to the WHH approach, and some won't. We typically see our students using this therapy about 1/4 of the time, alone or in combination with other therapies.

Basic WHH does not require any unusual abilities or states of consciousness, and so can be used by almost everyone regardless of their type of difficulty. Yet, the client still must be able to follow directions and be able to tolerate a certain amount of pain, which limits its usefulness. However, if the client has certain types of peak states, or can be induced into one, its speed drastically increases and the pain involved nearly vanishes. We'll be going into that in depth in this class.

What are some concrete examples of things that WHH is good for? Fear, physical pain, eating disorders, shame, sadness, anger, guilt, low self-confidence, grief, trauma, abuse, phobias, improved hearing and vision, stamina, more emotionally present with others, increased ability to give and receive love, profound spiritual experiences, and peak states of consciousness.

The Distant Personality Release (DPR) process

The basic WHH process works directly on trauma, which it turns out is typically the reason for a person's difficulty. However, there is another class of problems, ones that can be thought of as personality or inherited problems that have their origin at a non-physical level. We've developed a process that you can use on your clients, both to speed and ease their healing, and in some cases actually change their behavior without their participation. Some of the more fascinating applications are in making clients willing to heal, as in addiction cases. It's also particularly useful in couple's therapy, as it gives great compassion for the other partner's difficulties.

Trauma relief using the Inner Peace peak state process

As part of this workshop, we'll be putting you through a process that may result in giving you a relatively permanent peak state of consciousness, the Inner Peace state. This state is particularly valuable for therapists to use on clients, as it shuts off past emotional trauma from being felt in the present. If you are willing and the time is available, we may also try for more advanced states. As these states make you feel very comfortable, it can be difficult to find any issues to heal afterwards, so we'll be doing this towards the end of the workshop. This process unfortunately works only in about 50-60% of the people we've tried it on, so we can't guarantee that it will work for you. However, you will be able to compare notes with your classmates and see how these states affect them, what they're useful for, and so on.

We'll also be spending a lot of time explaining how these states are relevant to the basic WHH process, and how they appear in the general population.

How do the basic and advanced Whole-Hearted Healing trainings fit together?

The basic Whole-Hearted Healing class is required for the advanced Whole-Hearted Healing training. Advanced WHH requires that the practitioner have fairly unusual states of consciousness. In the required states, a practitioner can actually intervene in a client's consciousness, for example just as a shaman might do while doing a soul retrieval. This allows us to treat clients who will not or cannot take directions, such as the severely mentally ill, injured, or mentally handicapped, or who refuse to heal themselves for a variety of other reasons. It's particularly valuable for studying the causes for various conditions in our clients, and so we use it in our various Institute projects. Part of the training for this process is how to have these states of consciousness, and others too, and since our methods for inducing these states won't yet work on most people, this training is limited to people who can acquire the necessary states. Another part of this process is the healing necessary to merge with a client safely.

Fortunately, advanced WHH is not needed for a typical therapist. The basic process is adequate for the kinds of clients a therapist usually sees, as well as for people working on themselves. Typically, about 10% of our basic students have an interest in learning the advanced process.

ADMINISTRATIVE DETAILS & FORMS

We have some practical administrative details below to get out of the way before we go any further:

Personal list of issues

During our training, you'll be using your own issues to practice healing. Please make sure that you have at least 5 emotional issues, and a couple of physical issues written down—Appendix J has space for you to make this list for your reference during the workshop. Rate each issue on a scale of 0-10 for painfulness. This is very important not only to allow you to do work in a timely manner, but because if you enter a peak state, you may find you simply can't think of any issues because you don't feel bad anymore!

Background and peak state questionnaires

To get started with this class, we would appreciate it if you would fill out the background questionnaire that is in Appendix J and hand it in. This helps us in deciding what background material we need to present, as well as in the type of psychology 'jargon' that we can use. **IF YOU HAVE ANY POTENTIALLY SERIOUS HEALTH PROBLEMS OR ISSUES (LIKE CHEST PAIN OR HEART CONDITIONS), LET US KNOW IMMEDIATELY!** We suggest that people with a heart condition NOT take the workshop, just in case (we will give a full refund). If you have any physical conditions that might make these processes difficult to do, or might make your condition worsen, please let us know on the form. If this is the case, we expect you to work with your physician both before and after the workshop to be sure your condition doesn't worsen.

Part of the form asks how you found out about this work. Please be as explicit as you can, as it helps us know what works to reach people and what doesn't.

Please also fill out the form in Appendix K that we are currently using to evaluate your state of consciousness. We will be asking you to fill it out each morning, and probably several times during the peak state induction processes. At the end of the class, please hand it in. We will be using it for our research, in order to improve our processes and evaluate results. All results are confidential.

Group confidentiality

Much of what we'll be doing can involve very personal, very private material. Under no circumstances may you talk about a specific person's issue outside of class in such a way as they could be identified by someone else. It's the same sort of courtesy that you would wish for yourself if your circumstances were reversed. Often, it's difficult to tell what could feel invasive to another person, so as a general rule, apply this to ANYTHING that occurs in the workshop.

Liability form

For our own legal protection, we ask you to sign the liability form. Since our processes are often experimental, there is no guarantee that you might not have a problem with one or more of them. There is risk associated with this work, and if you are not willing to be responsible for whatever you experience in this work, we require you NOT to continue this workshop. A full refund will be given.

Additionally, some of our processes have not been either fully developed, or tested to our satisfaction, or they may be intrinsically dangerous. (It's a bit like either a homemade chain saw might explode in your hands, or a reliable store bought chain saw can be dangerous in the hands of untrained people even though as a tool it's well made).

Permission to videotape

In these workshops, we sometimes videotape sessions so that sometime in the future we can turn this material into a set of training videos. If you are OK with this, please sign the release forms. If you decide later on in the training that you're uncomfortable with that decision, feel free to change your mind, or make note of the specific incident you don't want presented to the public.

Please keep in mind that the pain you may have gone through in this workshop might be able to help someone else heal, or help them decide to heal. Thanks!

(Please fill out the form in Appendix J and hand it in when completed.)

Group introductions

You're in the presence of very unusual people, the kind that would be willing to come to a workshop like this. Please share with your colleagues something about your background, as well as what you hope to get out of this workshop. This latter part is particularly important, as we'll make note of it so as to cover it during our time together. Too, these people are ones you'll know the most about when we're done, and can act as referrals or consultants to your work in the future. We'll limit the time each person can speak to about 2 minutes - this is just to break the ice. You'll get to know each other very well in the next few days from working together.

Email and website practitioner lists

Please write down contact information (especially email addresses) on the contact form in Appendix J. We'll use this to put you on our very infrequent newsletter, and to invite you into the support email group that your WHH peers use. If you wish, include a short paragraph about yourself and your work to be put on our web site so that we can list you as a practitioner of WHH. If doing healing with others, on either a free or paid basis is appealing to you, please do so as we constantly get requests from clients looking for people either in their area or on the phone they can work with. By writing a short paragraph (and JPEG photo if possible), you are introducing yourself to potential clients who need your help. We suggest in your paragraph that you emphasize the type of client or health issue you specialize in or are the most interested in working with. Clients prefer to go to 'specialists' for their condition, just as you would!

Training evaluation

It's very, very, very helpful to get feedback on what worked, what didn't, what was important or useful, and what wasn't, so we can continually improve our training and manual. Please, please, please fill this form out by the end of the workshop (see Appendix J). Tell us both the good and the bad! If you give us permission, we would appreciate being able to put any testimonial that you write on the website.

This workshop is going to be hard work, but it can be really exhilarating at the same time with the company of your peers. Success!

Ask for help!

During the course of the workshop, *please* ask for assistance if you get stuck. And don't stop asking until you get it! As you will see, a lot is going on during the sessions, and we tend to assume if you aren't asking for assistance, you don't need it. Don't let your self-sufficiency, stoicism, shyness, or anything else get in the way of receiving everything you deserve from our time together.

Note for instructors

Because the amount of time that a session takes can be so variable, we've set up each day to that the WHH practice sessions are just before lunch and dinner breaks. This way, the participants can 'run over' the typical 30 minutes per session if they so desire. After the group reassembles, we recommend having each student describe what they did and learned during their work both as client and as therapist. We've found this can be very valuable for the other classmates.

We've included quiz solutions at the end of the manual. These can be removed before class if the instructors feel that this might be desirable.

During group sharing time with large groups, it's sometimes useful to set time limits, perhaps by using a talking stick and a bell timer.

We are continuously updating Appendix K, the peak state evaluation form. We don't expect you to use it in your workshops. However, if you would contact us to get the latest form and send us the results, we'd appreciate it greatly!

At the end of the manual is a brief description of the Hollow/Brightness peak state process. We've found it's very difficult to do this along with the rest of the material in four days, so this is generally done on a fifth day. As the steps are constantly being improved, we've omitted them (the 'Gaia Instructions') in this manual. Contact us for the latest steps—but due to the experimental nature of the process, we currently ask that you've already had advanced training (or equivalent - talk to me about this) in case something unexpected comes up in the class.

EXERCISE—THE HENDRICKS "LOVING YOURSELF" TECHNIQUE

The need to love yourself is often spoken about, but very few people give concrete advice on how to do it. Dr. Gay Hendricks in his book, The Learning to Love Yourself Workbook gives concrete methods and advice, and I highly recommend your read his book. But for now, we're going to learn and practice one of his techniques because it's very relevant for our work. The ability to love yourself, and teach it to your clients, makes the WHH process work faster and much more painlessly. Also, it often quickly and easily brings to consciousness memories that can't easily be accessed, and so it should be considered an important piece in your toolkit. As we're doing the process:

• Think about how you would teach it to clients quickly

• What you would do for clients who couldn't do it easily or at all

• Try and feel why it would be useful for healing, and why it might not be.

The process: recall something in your life that you can recall really loving. I would suggest a doll, or pet, rather than a significant other, because we want a pretty straightforward feeling, not one mixed up with rejection, punishment, etc. One woman had a favorite aunt that worked perfectly. Imagine this object is in front of you, and bring up that feeling of love you had for it. Stay with this until it's nice and strong. OK, now, turn that flow of love going outward back on yourself, like redirecting a hose of water. Sit with this until you've got it. Then let the person or object fade away while you continue to love yourself.

A variation of this is instead of redirecting the flow of loving feeling at yourself, you bring the person or object slowly into your body while you continue to love it. Once inside, you slowly let it dissolve while letting the loving feeling continue to fill you.

A second variation is to recall a favorite place, one that brings a really good feeling into your body, loving or otherwise. Use that as your trick to loving yourself.

Soon, we'll be doing the loving yourself technique while we do WHH on ourselves. Doing both at once can be a bit like juggling if you're not used to it, which is why I don't generally start by teaching this for the first healing experience. However, it can make the healing happen in just seconds, instead of minutes or hours, or can even help you face something you just can't from a cold start.

One interesting thing that can happen while using this technique is that your or your client's problem will simply go away while doing it! However, the problem has NOT been healed. It's simply been put back into storage as it were, and will come back out some other day. So you need to keep focused on the problem until you can find it again, and use WHH (or another therapy) on the issue till it's healed. To reiterate, the loving yourself process isn't intrinsically healing, but it facilitates healing processes that actually cure the problem.

Practice Session Notes:

ALL ABOUT THE INITIAL WHH SESSION

(See Appendix A for a sample client letter and intake form.)

When working on yourself, or your clients, what can you expect, and what can go wrong? For a moment, put yourself in your client's shoes. Imagine that you are that client, seeing a practitioner for the first time, and he's going to do this new therapy you've never heard of on you. In Appendix A, I give a sample letter that addresses these issues up front. Please take the time to read it now.

Of course, that letter is only a template for your own work, and feel free to rewrite it to fit your own circumstances. In an office situation, I find it's a good idea to give to clients before you start working with them, so they get an idea of what to expect both during and after the session.

One of the biggest problems with WHH, and in fact any power therapy, is that they work too well! As strange as it sounds, more that half of your clients (or you if you are working on yourself) are going to walk out of your office and by the next day are going to forget they ever had the problem they just paid you to heal! That's because, when they check in on themselves, there is no emotional charge anymore, and so it tends to feel like it never happened. Another variation of this is when they can recall they once had a problem, but they ascribe the solution to something familiar to them, like "I just forgot about it", or "I got distracted and it went away". This bizarre effect is called the "apex" phenomenon. For example, I've seen a person who was afraid to leave their home for over a decade completely forget that they'd ever had any trouble in doing so! The apex phenomenon can cause you problems in two ways. First, since the client doesn't recall they had a problem, they won't recommend your work, or come back to you for their next problem. The only thing we can recommend for this is to ALWAYS write down the client's presenting problem along with a 0-10 scale (the SUDS - Standard Units of Distress Scale) on how bad it was. If you can tape or video the session, so much the better.

A few other common questions that come up before the first session are:

- Can using WHH on old painful memories "re-traumatize" me? The answer is no. This is a very reasonable question, as conventional psychotherapy can do exactly that. If they don't actually finish healing something, you can truthfully congratulate them on removing some of the charge on what they were working on, leaving less for the next time.

- Another common question is if this work will be OK with other therapies? The answer is yes, and in fact I recommend it. The only problem you might find is impatience with other work that doesn't give as fast a result!

I want to take a moment here to emphasize some of the potential problems of the WHH technique. They happen very rarely, but you should be aware of them. If you have other power therapies in your 'toolkit' and you run into trouble, that might be a good time to dust them off and use them on your suffering client.

- The emotional and/or physical pain that comes up from remembering some of these things is usually worse than the emotional pain a client comes in with. The next layer down in the trauma stack may be much more severe than the one you started with. Suddenly, the client might be feeling a whole host of injuries that they didn't feel before you started. This is to be expected, and means that you have to persevere. Occasionally when working alone, you might find that you are not able to face the material by yourself, and end up feeling pretty awful for a while. So if someone gets to an old trauma but is unsuccessful taking off any of the charge, they may leave in misery. Of course, it eventually fades just as it did originally, but it can be a problem for someone not used to healing. Fortunately, the person recognizes it as coming from their own lives, and I haven't had any problems with people blaming me for stirring up old stuff.

- In a few cases when you do heal some trauma with someone, the next thing they know some physical (and/or emotional) pain arises from earlier memories that needs to be healed. If you don't get to the memory that's driving it, from the client's perspective they walk away with a "new'" physical pain that they never had before. Of course, it will fade with time just as it did originally, but if you don't finish your work, they can leave you in more distress than they walked in with. This can especially occur with traumas involving soul loss or holes, which will be covered later in the class.

- Many therapists will only see a client for a scheduled 50 minutes. I recommend leaving the sessions more open-ended than that, as sometimes the client will just take more time than that to heal. There can be several problems with stopping too soon - the client walks out feeling worse than they did when they walked in, which does not make you popular with your client and can certainly harm your reputation as a wonderful healer; new memories, such as sexual abuse, can surface (worse yet, if the memories still feel traumatic, the client might decide to shoot their perpetrator when they remember the event for the first time); and it can be very difficult to get a client back to an old trauma, especially if it occurred before conscious memory. If you warn people **ahead of time** that this might happen, and explain to your clients that the session before theirs might take longer than expected, clients generally are OK with it - after all, that could be themselves in there!

- I **DON'T** recommend that the typical client go looking for traumas to heal when there isn't some problem in the present that's up for them. This is especially true when dealing with birth trauma. If you don't heal it all the way, the client will suddenly have new problems in their life when they walk out the door. So, work from current issues, don't go looking for trouble! (If you do decide to go 'trolling', which is what we call this, please read the section on how to do it correctly.)

Another issue that can initially come up around this work has to do with legal and insurance problems. Laws differ from state to state and from country to country, so you will need to pursue this on your own. The problem is two fold - since WHH is considered a "non-standard" therapy, a licensed therapist can (potentially) be sued for using it. On the opposite extreme, a non-licensed person might be sued or have trouble with the authorities because they are 'practicing therapy without a license'. Since this is a generic problem with many therapies, not just WHH, I suggest you ask around for how others in your area deal with it. Another successful strategy that a number of people employ is to get a ministerial license. See the material in Day 4 for a recommendation there.

Finally, I'm going to get on my soapbox for a moment. I believe that if you do charge clients, you should offer some sort of money back guarantee and to charge by the problem, not by the amount of time it takes you. (Make sure they write down their issue and how bad it is first though, since half of them are liable to forget they had the problem due to the apex phenomenon.) Current practice in therapy and medicine is to charge for time, not results. This was a natural response to the fact that the methods in current practice don't work well. However, with WHH, or any power therapy for that matter, you should be getting fast and permanent results. And offering a money back guarantee will certainly motivate you to a high level of success, as well as give you great ethical satisfaction. One might argue that once a client learns the technique, they won't return, and the therapist will starve. But with WHH or other power therapies, you're not only offering a method to empower people, you're offering your healed self which makes their healing easier since they unconsciously feel safe enough to feel their pain. And your expertise can greatly help people through some of the twists of resistance that comes up. I've made a point of this here because in my experience with therapists, when I suggest they offer a guarantee, they get very upset. If you're a therapist reading this, I strongly recommend you heal any resistance you might have to this idea, if just for your peace of mind.

The sample intake form is just a reminder to get client information. Issue and severity are included so you have a record of what you've done to remind your client later. Don't forget to find out if they have unusual physical conditions like heart trouble, which would impact your work with them. Also note generational issues, (i.e. problems common to the family and ancestors) as it may make a difference in your approach.

Key Points:

- Clients can feel worse during the healing.

- The apex phenomenon affects how to work with clients.

- Why it's a bad idea to stop before the healing is finished.

THE WHH PROCESS—FIRST DEMONSTRATION & DISCUSSION

We're doing a demonstration of the process before we teach you how, just to demonstrate how we go about it with a new client. If one of you would volunteer to be a demo subject, that would be great! As we work, take notes on what strikes you as important. Since this is a demonstration, we probably won't go to completion on the issue due to time constraints.

As we work, there are several things the observers and the therapist can do to make the healing go faster and easier in the client. Over the next few days, we'll be learning several of them, but for now the biggest problem people have in healing isn't the pain of their issue—it's the unconscious reaction that the therapist (and observers) have to the client's experience and feelings. Essentially, a client approaches these painful experiences, and unconsciously checks in with the therapist to get an idea of how bad it is. If the therapist has a similar problem, and is unconsciously telling the client that "This trauma we're feeling is really bad", the client has a much more difficult time healing. At a deep level, you look to the other person for support and safety, and if they've suddenly freaked out (even if they don't know it), something inside you says that "This trauma must be even worse than I thought, and I better not mess with it!" The converse is also true - somebody who has healed similar stuff can help you feel safe enough to face it. For example, during holotropic breath sessions, a friend of mine has seen people go into birth trauma after Dr. Stanislav Grof (the originator of the method) walked up to them. As he moved away, they would leave that experience. These people could not hear or see him, since they were blindfolded and loud music was playing. Although any particular client could just ignore the therapist and heal it anyway, it's very common that healing doesn't take place in the client.

Thus, in our experience, there are ONLY three reasons why a client doesn't heal in your presence:

- You have a trauma that is similar to the client's.

- You unconsciously don't want the client to heal, perhaps because they remind you of someone like they are right now and you don't want them to change.

- You don't have a good enough technique or use it incorrectly.

Generally, reason #1 is almost always the problem. It's almost never #3. Thus, our clients are actually paying us to see where we have problems, and ethically it's our responsibility to see that we are as healed as possible when working with them - or at least, we send them home while we do our own personal work.

Case #2 isn't as common as case #1, but it's very fascinating. This happens with someone you have a unconscious, interlocking agreement not to change with. I have an old friend who just wasn't healing with these procedures while I was with her. Nothing changed until one day I realized she reminded me of my mom at a particular time, and I didn't want her to be any different. The next time we tried healing, it worked!

What can we do as healers to avoid this problem? First, if it's easy enough, we whip through healing our similar issue while they're still struggling. Since this isn't always an option, the easiest method is to use the 'loving yourself' technique. This tends to turn off our response to the clients trauma and thus assists them in healing.

As we do the session, take special notice of the following points:.

- Enough explanation so the client feels the process makes sense to them.

- The timing of steps of the process - how practice gives you a feel for when to intervene.

- Watch their bodies and their reactions to the work.

- Notice how you felt during their process inside your own body

Key Points:

- Use the 'loving yourself' technique to assist your clients' healing.

- If the client doesn't heal quickly, check for a similar or interlocking problem in yourself.

- Test for calm, peace, and lightness (CPL) to see if your client has fully healed the current trauma and issue.

Notes of First Demonstration:

Notes on First Demonstration (continued):

THE BASIC WHOLE-HEARTED HEALING (WHH) PROCESS

(See Appendix B for an outline of the basic WHH steps. I suggest that you refer to it as you read this section. It can be very useful in the future when you need to remind yourself on the steps and what to do for unusual problems during a therapy session!)

Whole-Hearted Healing is considered a trauma healing technique based on regression. In practice, it is used primarily for emotional healing, although it works on many physical problems because they are related to trauma. First of all, what do I mean by emotional healing? It turns out that almost everyone's feelings about current situations in their lives are actually from past traumas. I've found that when the relevant past is healed, the person's feelings about their current difficulty simply vanish. A person who is actually in the present has an underlying sense of calm, peace, and lightness (CPL) even while feeling difficult emotions. (This is in contrast to feeling calm and heavy, which is when you are suppressing and denying how you feel.) This means that the technique works for **ANYTHING** that you don't feel calm, peace and light about. For example, a man with a painful and terminal gut cancer didn't feel calm and light with his apparently reasonable fear of dying, and so proceeded to heal it in one session.

The indented material below is what I typically say to a person learning the Whole-Hearted Healing technique for the first time.

> "So, pick something that's bugging you. Allow yourself to feel how you feel about it as much as possible. Then, allow your mind to drift into the past, as far back in the past as you can, to a time when you had the SAME feeling. Now, it probably won't be the same circumstances, the ONLY important thing is the same feeling. I'll emphasize again that it will almost never be the same sort of situation that you are in right now, rather the influence from the past is a connection of feeling only."

> "OK, got that image of some time in the past? Now, try and go even further back, to a time when you FELT the same. Keep doing this till you can't go back any further. Why? Because it turns out that we only have to heal the earliest time, in general. Heal the first one, and the rest go poof by themselves. If you can't recall that far back, no sweat - go as far back as you can, and as you heal it, any earlier time will generally just pop into mind, until you get to the first one that way. So, say you get stuck, and can't recall anything. Just go back, even if it's only last week, and start from there. Pull off those traumas one at a time to work back into the past. It's just like in a cafeteria, with those plate dispensers. You know, where you pull one from the top, and the spring pushes the stack up. These traumas are just like that - as you heal one, the one that's earlier pops into view. Jump to a plate in the middle, and you remove all the plates above it. Occasionally, the structure is more complicated, and your current problem comes from more that one place, but the single stack of trauma's with an emotional theme is pretty common."

> "At this point, I would recommend that you write down just briefly what's happening in the present that bugs you, how bad you feel about it, and a quick description of the memories you've recalled. Why? Because if we do it right, this stuff will disappear out of your life, and like many people I've worked with, you won't be able to believe you ever had a problem, and so you'll not continue healing because you think nothing happened!"

If you are interested in how traumas connect together (and a different power therapy healing technique that is also very effective called 'Traumatic Incident Reduction'), I recommend reading *Traumatic Incident Reduction* By Gerald French and Chrys Harris, or the much more difficult to read *Beyond Psychology* by Dr. Frank Gerbode. See also Dr. Stanislav Grof's work on the coex system (and birth trauma), such as *The Adventure of Self Discovery*. Incidentally, both Dr. Gerbode, and Drs. Gay and Kathlyn Hendricks (*At the Speed of Life*) using quite different techniques from mine have also concluded that specific traumas are the root of our issues, rather than some sort of soaking effect from a bad environment.

It turns out that we all share a critical 'blind spot' around healing. This insight is not in any literature that I know of. It's so ordinary to us, we don't see its significance. This is the key insight to understanding how traumatic memories are stored.

> "So, now to the crux of how to heal. Take a look at those traumatic memories. They're like watching TV, aren't they? In other words, your viewpoint is outside of your body, not out of your eyes (some people are aware that it's both). THIS IS THE PROBLEM. A part of us has the ability to leave our body during painful times, and naturally enough does. Unfortunately, the feelings we had at that time stay with us and never go away! They just lie around waiting until something in the present triggers them again."

Thus, the mechanism for the storage of traumatic emotions is the out-of-body experience (OBE), in the form of an image(s) stored at the moment of trauma. In fact, as you go through your day you can become aware that these images flash into consciousness and out again so fast we typically aren't aware of them, but they guide our behavior. This can be demonstrated by using GSR (galvanic skin response) meters as feedback devices to give us practice in noticing the phenomena.

Since our culture in general does not accept the existence of the out-of-body experience, most therapies assume these images are just distortions of past memories, and don't look any closer. However, people who do recognize the existence of the out-of-body experience make a different mistake. They assume its a rare occurrence, when in actuality it's happening all the time. What's rare about it is being aware of it in the present, but we can easily be aware of it in the past by scanning our painful memories. Occasionally, individuals find it difficult to notice the out-of-body part of the image. For them, I have them recall something really traumatic in their life to demonstrate the principle.

This insight has stunning implications! For example, it predicts that people who had their eyes closed, or even people who are blind (assuming no brain damage) have a 'visual' image of the trauma, something that conventional science would declare is impossible. This prediction has actually been discovered in the last few years, and is described in the book Mindsight by Dr. Kenneth Ring.

Now, how to use this insight in healing:

> "To heal this memory, all you do is reverse what happened. Instead of leaving your body, you go into it in the past AND FEEL WHAT YOU DIDN'T WANT TO FEEL THE FIRST TIME. So, how to do this? It turns out that there is only one critically important place in our body that we must stay in, in order to heal - that is in the center of the chest, about midway between the nipples. The simplest way to understand what I want you to do is to place and keep your hand on your chest there, in the present. This gives you a body sensation in the present to remind you of what it feels like to be in your chest, while you're in the past. So, go back to that image in the past where you went out of your body. You will notice that you can move your viewpoint around at will. Try moving left, then right, to demonstrate this to yourself. Now, move yourself straight back into your body in the past, looking out of your eyes at what was happening, feeling your body as it was, and ESPECIALLY STAYING IN YOUR CHEST IN THE PAST."

A small percentage of people have great difficulty in seeing the images, or in fact any image at all, but fortunately the WHH process still works, it's just a bit harder for them since they have to feel they are in their body without any visual feedback.

The second critical insight to healing is realizing that an individual 'leaves their body' from the center of their chest. The 'hand on chest' technique is a big help to about 2/3 of the people I see, drastically increasing people's understanding of what I want them to do. Getting people to stay in their bodies, and specifically their chest in the past during trauma is, in my opinion, what most successful healing modalities are trying to accomplish—they just don't know it! It's the 'hidden co-variable' of most healing techniques, and I believe often explains why sometimes a therapy works, and sometimes it doesn't.

Body centered therapy which uses breath may be taking advantage of an indirect method for returning to the body. I've found that in severe trauma when it was very difficult to bring oneself back in, by building up an oxygen surplus then returning to the trauma it often becomes very easy. I speculate that this is relaxing a concurrently activated core birth trauma involving oxygen deprivation and injury to the solar plexus which first initiated uncontrolled out of body activity. This observation also suggests that using supplemental oxygen would facilitate healing trauma.

We've also discovered that trauma is stored during the OBE experience when the diaphragm stiffens. Thus, one can have an OBE that doesn't store trauma, but if there is trauma storage, the diaphragm had a momentary (or lengthy, of course) hardening while in the OBE.

"Now, allow yourself to feel what happened. Sometimes this is much easier to say than to do, because we didn't want to feel it in the first place. Whatever you do, don't try and change the past. Not only doesn't this work, it causes you not to heal. Just accept what happened. So, if you do this, a very interesting thing happens. It's just like you are draining a cup of (emotional) liquid through a tube. With some practice, you can actually feel the emotion flowing into your chest and dissolving there, like your chest was some sort of drain. Regardless of whether you feel that or not, as you stay with the feeling, suddenly it just runs out and ends. Now, one of 3 things happens then. You either 1) feel peaceful, calm, and lightness; 2) another feeling that was hidden under the last one comes up, and you just drain it away too, like pealing layers of an onion; 3) an earlier memory arises, and you skip to that one to heal."

When I first started using this technique, I assumed that I was simply erasing a complex memory. Now, I've concluded that I'm actually in the past changing it in 'real time', in a limited way. This has tremendous implications in understanding how the past, future, and present interact, and I go into this in more detail further in the course.

The 'draining' mechanism is fascinating. It can be drastically speeded up using several other techniques, but I usually don't teach them initially, as it becomes too difficult to hold all the instructions at once.

Notice too that I do NOT recommend giving any sort of positive affirmation or advice to the client. In general, I feel the only use for positive affirmations is to flush up the resistance to them in order to heal it.

However, dealing with the emotional part of trauma is not enough. Two other factors are critical to successful healing:

"There is another, important part to this. As you heal, pay attention to your thoughts in the past. Each incident has at least one short phrase associated with it, usually from 2 to 6 words (for example, "I'm stupid."). It's very important you catch and really be aware of the phrase that's been running your life ever since. It can be true or false, specific or a generalization - but the problem is that we take it and apply it to everything in our lives indiscriminately ever afterwards.

Additionally, you have to feel how your body felt, i.e. stomach tension, or the pain of an injury, etc. Like the emotions, you have to feel this until it fades to nothing also. I'm sort of glossing over this, but as you can imagine it can be excruciatingly painful at times.

So, to review - put your hand on your chest, go into your body in the past, feel the emotions until they are gone, notice the phrase that you said to yourself at the time, and feel the body sensations until they are gone too. We recommend that you stay in the trauma even after you believe it's all gone for about another three minutes, as there is sometimes subtle or painful material that is still suppressed from awareness, or unusual spiritual or healing events need extra time to complete."

It turns out that usually each trauma has a whole constellation of phrases that tie into the traumatic feelings, but the one that occurred during the trauma itself holds all the others in place. Getting the core phrase eliminates all the associated material that is tied into it. If you don't bring the phrase into consciousness, you find that the feeling cannot be completely drained away. Especially in severe trauma, you feel a sudden intensification of physical or emotional symptoms when you get close to the exact phrase. For example, while I was working on a severe injury at 11 months of age, when I thought "Can't trust mom!", I'd suddenly lose my breath. Later, the correct phrase popped up, "Can't trust women!", and the whole trauma released. The phrase matches the body sensation, in effect putting words to how our body feels. For a more in depth discussion of what this means, it is described as the 'felt sense' in Eugene Gendlin's *Focusing*, where methods to practice it are described.

A variety of healing techniques focus on a part of the whole picture, but to completely heal trauma, the contributions from every part of us (the mind, heart, and body) must be addressed. It appears to me that storage of traumatic material is an out of control survival mechanism present in us and all other animal species.

"So, how do you know if you are done? The image should have dissolved, so that you are just in your body in the past, looking out of your eyes. The feelings from the incident should be all gone, as if you were rereading last year's stock pages from the newspaper. As a test, if you try a quick peek at the memory, it won't have any little painful twinge. Come back to the present, and see if whatever was bothering you (how this all started) now is at peace. If it isn't, either the trauma you've worked on isn't finished, or there is another earlier memory that needs healing. The earliest memory always involves physical damage or injury to the body. Stick with the healing process until you are completely at peace in the present."

"Finally, a natural question that comes up is what to do if you get interrupted, or just can't finish for some other reason, or flat out can't take the pain anymore. Good news! Remember the analogy that I started with, about draining a cup of emotional liquid? This is actually pretty accurate, and so if you do some healing on a trauma, that leaves just that much less feeling you have to feel later. Nor will the amount of emotional pain fill back up while you wait so that you're back to where you started from. However, if you do take a break, be sure to make a written note so that you can remember to go back and finish it off later."

What are the potential drawbacks to this healing technique? First, it's intrinsically painful. Second, the emotional and physical pain that can come up from remembering your past is usually worse than the pain you start the process with. So if you don't finish healing a trauma, for a while you may end up feeling worse than when you started. Third, on very rare occasions a physical or emotional pain may appear as if from nowhere, as an earlier trauma 'beneath' the one you're working comes partially to consciousness. Completely healing the trauma you're on, and using other techniques such as Hendrick's 'loving yourself' will generally bring the new trauma to clarity, but not always. Fortunately in any case the pain fades just as it did originally. Therapists trained in advanced Whole-Hearted Healing techniques can assist in healing these sorts of trauma by merging with the client and healing them directly. However, those techniques are beyond the scope of this manual.

We've found that all *in utero* trauma ALWAYS has physical injury associated with it, due to the unusual nature of fetal consciousness. Persevere until the client not only gets to CPL, but feels very large *in utero* everywhere. After birth, an event can be traumatic without physical injury. This has to do with the change in the kind of consciousness we have at birth. Be sure to persevere to the real origin points.

Common initial mistakes

The biggest mistake people make is not staying with it until all the feelings are gone. This is a perfectly natural reaction, because we've all had the experience of recalling a painful memory, and it just won't go away, so we just try and forget it. (I wished forgetting really worked, but unfortunately the trauma just lies there like a land mine for later in our life.) To account for this problem, I now have the clients stay an extra three minutes in body after we think we are finished, just to make sure there isn't anything else to be flushed up.

Another key mistake people make is that they go out-of-body again when they recall this stuff, just like the first time, so of course it doesn't go away. We just do the same thing over again! I can't repeat enough times, **YOU HAVE TO STAY IN YOUR CHEST IN THE PAST.**

Another mistake happens when the person doesn't stay focused at the time of the image, and sort of wanders around the moment that's so painful. It's a sort of skipping in and out of the painful moment, or a sort of unintentional blurring. This certainly prolongs the pain, and probably for most people stops healing altogether. A less common variation of this is to jump around to a bunch of traumas, like channel surfing on TV, but not stay with any of them for long enough to heal. If you have multiple symptoms from different traumas at the same time, choose the one that feels most insistent first, and stay with it until it's gone before moving to the next.

The other common mistake people make is to go into negative judgment about what happened. You know, like "I shouldn't have done that", or "How could I have felt that way", or... Going into a negative judgment just adds to the problem. Instead, an attitude of acceptance (or better yet, an attitude of self-love, as it has acceptance in it) for yourself is what is necessary. One problem I occasionally run into is people who try and think understanding and forgiving thoughts from their perspective now, rather than what they really thought then. The opposite can be true too, as happens when you think only condemning thoughts about someone, when what you actually thought at the time may have been one of loss or grief. Fortunately, just bringing the phrase to consciousness along with releasing the emotion is enough to eliminate it from your life, and there is no need to try and fix how you felt, thought, or acted.

> **Example:** Paula was regressed to a pre-birth trauma. There was an insoluble dilemma—the zygote couldn't make up its mind to jump into the uterus or just stall there. Paula was strongly tempted to 'fix' it by making the zygote jump, because from her adult perspective she knew this was the right thing to do. Instead, she correctly stayed with the trauma and a completely different outcome took place. Instead of perceiving the womb as a huge void chamber, it suddenly became a life filled ocean into which she joyfully dived.

Another, although much less frequent mistake occurs when a person tries to talk about the painful feelings they're having, a sort of classical therapy approach. Unfortunately, many people use talking as a defense to feeling, and so nothing will heal till they quit doing this. These people need to stop intellectualizing while working on old painful experiences until after they heal them. Talking in general while healing is fine, as long as it doesn't become a block to feeling.

A really tricky way to NOT heal occurs when people try to love themselves in the past by embracing their past selves with love, sort of like a parent does with a child. The mistake here is that you have to merge with yourself in the past, become yourself, and not stay outside by giving hugs!

One person I worked with had the idea that she was trying to contain her feelings in her chest when I told her to stay in her chest - sort of like putting those painful feelings in prison. When you go into the past, you need to make sure you don't go out-of-body, and the place you go out-of-body from is your chest. However, you need to feel your whole body in the past, because that's where the emotions are!

Speeding the healing

If you can feel real love for yourself while you're simultaneously feeling traumatic material, it will radically speed the healing process. In severe trauma I've also found that doing this brings people into their bodies who can't do it otherwise. Finally, it will often help you to recall the traumatic memories you need to heal. Again, I refer you to Dr. Gay Hendrick's technique found in the book *The Learning to Love Yourself Workbook*.

The second technique is more unusual. So, while you go back to the trauma, pretend that your body, especially your chest, is full of light. Imagine that there are balls of clear white light in your head, chest and lower belly, and that you are those balls of light. Being that ball of white light in your chest is the most important part. White light is how a part of us perceives unobstructed self-awareness. In addition, try and feel like your body is huge with your viewpoint from the inside of your body. If you can, try and feel that you are whole, or complete, just as you are. By this I don't mean healed - that comes later. And finally, it might help if you can pull in a sense of a greater presence. Then go for the feeling you had trouble with. Experiment with this a bit, because what you're trying to do is become aware (even a tiny bit) of how you experienced yourself in the womb, so you can be like that again to make the healing easier. The part about the light inside you is actually true all the time, as is the greater presence, it's just blocked from your awareness. See if you can work it until it starts to feel natural. I'd like to give credit to Dr. Andrew Terker for my adaptation of his technique.

Certain peak states of consciousness speed up the healing drastically (the Hollow, Wholeness, and Gaia Awareness states for example). One way to get the same effect without having a peak state in the present is as follows: if, during the course of your work, you can recall a womb memory that was experienced without trauma (you feel large and filled with light in the womb), try and superimpose those sensations to the trauma you are trying to heal. This can drastically speed up the process. (Incidentally, the basic WHH process is actually just a way to simulate how you would heal a trauma if you had a peak state, but by doing it a step at a time rather than all at once.)

Key Points:

- Trauma (generally forgotten) as central to emotional issues in the present

- OBE as the storage mechanism for trauma

- CPL - Calm, peace, and lightness as an endpoint to healing

- Trauma generally has emotions in layers like an onion

- Traumas connect to each other by following a sensation theme to the origin

TRICKS AND SUBTLETIES OF WHH: WHAT TO DO IF THE TRAUMA WON'T RELEASE

As you do this healing work, you'll usually have the experience of the emotional and physical pain you're working on come to a clean and definite end. However, some traumas just don't feel as neat and tidy as this. The emotion doesn't quit, or it kind of lingers on, without a definite end point. About 10% of the people have this happen the first time I work with them. After I run through every possibility that I can think of, I ask them to try and heal some other problem. I want them to get a clear experience of healing something, so that they know what healing feels like. With that experience, they can trust that this type of healing works, and then we can go back and figure out what went wrong.

I assume that you know what healing feels like, but have met up with this problem. It turns out that there can be a variety of reasons why this happens. A common one occurs because we have the idea that whatever we're feeling is not OK. For example, one woman felt that sadness was not OK to feel because her mom used to go on and on with sadness. Before she could release her sadness, she had to first heal her revulsion at feeling sad. In my own case, I had the same sense of revulsion to my anger, due to an anesthesia experience during birth. So, I suggest that if you have a particular emotion that you can't release, you first look for some trauma in your life that made you decide that it wasn't OK for you to feel that way.

Probably the biggest problem in releasing severe trauma occurs because the exact wording of the trauma phrase isn't brought into consciousness. For example, when I was healing a severe blow to my head as a baby, the trauma just wouldn't release. As I tried different phrases, the discomfort in my solar plexus and belly would increase as I got closer to the correct one. Thus, the phrase "Can't trust mom" made me lose my breath, but the trauma still wouldn't release. It wasn't until I got the exact wording, "Can't trust women", that the trauma suddenly released.

One of the most powerful methods I know of is to put the client into the same physical position as occurred during the trauma, and if possible to make the same physical motion, slowly and gently. This can make someone who is not able to heal and be in body do so, or it can speed the healing of someone who is able to heal already. For example, for *in utero* traumas put the client into the fetal position. Or say in a car accident trauma, put them in the same position (along with being sideways or upside down or whatever) they had at the moment they're working on. For more on this, I refer you to Dr. Gay Hendrick's book, "*At the Speed of Life*", and his body centered approach to healing.

Another technique was discovered by one of my clients. As I mentioned, clenching the diaphragm while having an OBE is what locks the trauma in place. She found that she could reverse this process by having the client lay on their backs with their knees up with the sole of the feet flat. They would put their attention on their feet (grounding), while the therapist gently massages the diaphragm into relaxing while the client focuses on the trauma they're working on. This causes blocked emotions to dramatically flow through the client and release while doing the WHH process. A variation of this that a person can do on their own is as follows: round your pelvis up off of the ground as high as you can comfortably go (this with your knees bent, and your feet on the ground/bed) and then completely relaxing the pelvis, back, and abdominal muscles, let the body "whumpf" to the ground.

Another technique comes again from Dr. Gay Hendrick's book, *Conscious Breathing*. You have the client lie down (on the floor, on the massage table, etc.), and the therapist sits at their head with his hands palming the top-front part of their head in such a fashion that his fingers are draped across the client's forehead and his fingertips are touching their eyebrows. He then talks them through the trauma, having them focus on their feelings and thoughts, while at the same time making sure they are breathing through these feelings and thoughts. Of course, we'd add WHH by making sure the client was in body in the past while this was going on.

Timing can be important to one's healing. One woman I've worked with has told me she's found she'll occasionally get a certain sort of feeling in her chest, and at those times healing comes to her easily. It turns out that the easiest time to heal is when you're feeling the most miserable! Those feelings in the present are putting you as close to the original pain as possible. Waiting until you're calmer or have the time will often make it impossible to get at the feeling in the trauma. After all, who wouldn't unconsciously resist feeling bad if they're feeling OK now?

I've also found the best time for me to heal is early in the morning, just after I wake while still sleepy and in bed. This is because my conscious thoughts don't get in the way as much. Often, a trauma phrase will pop into my mind while I'm half asleep, when it won't when I'm wide awake. It also makes it easier for me to get into the fetal position, or whatever posture I was in when the trauma occurred, which can greatly enhance the process. In fact, I've discovered that I'll get really sleepy during the day when some traumatic memory is trying to surface. Taking a nap usually lets it come to consciousness when I wake. But watch out, I once had the opposite experience of trying to sleep to get away from the experience that was trying to come up!

I'll remind you again to use the loving yourself technique. It's simple, but very powerful. A variation on this is to recall a physical place where you felt especially good, bring this feeling up in yourself, and then go for the memory.

Combining WHH with other power therapies is another very effective way to speed or accomplish healing (see the day 3 section of this manual). In particular, the best technique I know of for finding the emotional and physical pain in a memory that you know must be present but can't feel is called 'Traumatic Incident Reduction (TIR)' or 'viewing' for short. It's taught by the Institute for Metapsychology in Menlo Park, California, and I highly recommend it and the other courses they teach. Essentially, what you do is just run over the entire trauma moment by moment, in as much detail as you can. You consciously start just before the trauma began, run through the incident, then repeat it again and again as many times as is necessary. Generally one finds that nothing hurts at first, more of the memory comes to light, then the pain increases, reaches a crescendo, and quickly ends. Staying in your chest and body speeds the process. I've found this technique invaluable with certain trauma's I just couldn't feel. More on this later.

A few traumas just won't completely release when you just focus on your own experience in it. You have to also be aware of how the other person in the event was affected by what happened, and feel their feeling. This is enough to let the last of it go. *In utero*, this is especially common due to the connection between the fetus and the parents. Especially *in utero*, the opposite problem can occur:

> **Example:** Paula found that during *in utero* trauma, if she expands her awareness to her mom, she can discriminate between her feelings and her mothers. This avoids the problem of mistakenly trying to heal her mother's feelings when it's her own material she has to feel. Usually they are related emotions, which makes it an easy mistake to make. Then the trauma releases quickly after this.

Interestingly, just reminding the client that their past self will and did survive this trauma is often enough to cause them to go in body and heal.

I encourage you to use other healing modalities like EFT, EMDR, holotropic breathwork, bodywork, other power therapies or whatever strikes your fancy. As the course progresses, we'll be covering more of the potential ways to ease and complete healing.

Copies

Another problem can occur when you run across a trauma that involves a 'copy'. Occasionally, you'll run into memories, especially early ones, where feeling the feeling just doesn't change anything. And unfortunately, you can feel these feelings forever and they won't go away. This occurs because this particular feeling is actually someone else's that you copied from them during a moment of trauma in your life. In these situations, you feel what someone around you felt as if it were your own emotion and/or body sensation or pain.

First, how does copying occur? During a crisis, you go out-of-body, as you know. But if you zip over to another beings heart region, their emotion gets stored as if it were your own. Fortunately, most people quit doing this at a pretty early age, so you won't have to worry about it too often. So, how do you heal this? You have to become aware of what your own body really felt at that time, and heal that. The copied emotions will just dissolve away - you might even feel them moving outward, away from your body.

How do you know if you're feeling a copy? Copied feelings can be either easy or hard to spot. Copied emotions have a subtle identifying 'tone' to them, as if the person were present in your own body where the emotion is. This can be pretty hard to spot at times, so if the healing is taking an unusually long time without any progress, try the following trick: guess what someone else would have felt in those circumstances, and gently try that on in your own body. For example, if you're feeling sad when most people would have been angry in your situation, try anger on for size. If you've copied, this usually triggers a much stronger response as you throw off the copy and become aware of your own feelings.

In my case, I could tell when I copied stuff from my dad, because the feeling had a sort of a Dad tone to it. It was much harder to tell in the case of my mother, because at birth I identified my emotional self with mom, and this was reinforced growing up because she was my 'safe' parent. It's taken me a long time to get better at spotting mom copies.

These copies can cause a tremendous amount of suffering. In later sections, we'll describe how these things have caused people to smoke, and often appear in chronic injuries like 'frozen shoulder' and chronic pain.

Another way to deal with copies is to get a client to realize that the symptom has over top of it on the skin level a feeling of someone else's personality. Using EFT on the idea that the client is actually holding on to the personality piece, rather than being a helpless victim, is generally enough to release it. However, as we note later on in the manual, EFT can be reversed. Thus, its use in this case should be weighted carefully. I believe at this time that the EFT does a great job of causing the client to release the copy. However, the underlying trauma that caused the person to copy in the first place is still there, and might be activated later. If it is, the client would again do a copy, perhaps with a different symptom, at some later date - just as they did originally. Of course, you could just tap it away again using EFT. Hence, given the client situation, you should evaluate how you want to proceed given these tradeoffs.

'Copying' appears to be a limited form of unconscious 'soul stealing' as described in a section in Day 2. We're still investigating this, as there might be another phenomenon involved. Copying only occurs after birth, although the traumas that set it up occur *in utero* or earlier.

Key Points:

• In severe trauma, the block is usually getting the exact phrase correctly.

• One of the simplest aids in experiencing difficult to feel trauma is to assume the same body position as occurred in the trauma.

• Relaxing the diaphragm, or hyperventilation, usually eases the release of trauma.

- 'Copies' from other people cannot be drained away. Instead, one's own feeling needs to be felt to release them.

TRICKS AND SUBTLETIES OF THE WHH THERAPY: WHAT TO DO IF YOU CAN'T RECALL THE TRAUMA

Say you're miserable in the present, and no earlier incident pops up when you look in the past. Fortunately, there are several things you can do. First, use the 'loving yourself' technique on what you're feeling. This tends to blow off steam, and much of the time an earlier memory will surface. This works so well that I rarely have to do anything else, other than encourage them to give themselves a little time to remember. Next, examine your beliefs about what's happening. Have you been assuming it was Dad (or Mom) stuff because of the sex of the person involved, or because everything you've got has always been Dad's (or Mom's) fault? For example, a friend of mine was convinced it was her Dad stuff, and got nowhere. Once she let go of preconceptions, it turned out it was an incident with a second grade female teacher. Again, the only important thing is to follow the feeling back into the past, not the circumstances.

Another thing that you might try is looking in the immediate past, not long ago. What if your misery is of recent origin? Even if it isn't, something that happened yesterday or last week can give you a 'first plate in the stack' entry into the sequence of traumas. From there, you can work backwards in time.

Occasionally, you (or the client) will attempt to work on an issue, but your attention is actually firmly fixed on some other issue, perhaps something that just happened in your life. Although many people can work anyway, some people or some people with particularly attention grabbing issues (such as a fight with the spouse just before the session) will find that they need to switch issues to the one that has their present time attention. Along these lines, I suggest students in our workshops work on the issue that is the biggest or worst right at the moment (the highest rating on a scale of 0 to 10).

I've also found that outside circumstances play a huge role in helping me heal. When something gets triggered, that's the best time to look for the traumatic memory. It turns out that the memory will often just pop up when we look for it when we feel our worst, because we're closest to the original experience. In fact, I've found that I'll unconsciously put myself in situations that make me feel worse and worse just so I can access these memories! However, be warned—if a traumatic memory comes up, and I decide to wait till later, occasionally I can't get back to the memory or the feeling of the memory. This has been a hard lesson at times! So now I just take the time to find an inconspicuous spot, put my hand on my chest, and go for it. At other times, just being out in the world will give me the inspiration I need to find a lost memory. For example, I was looking at why my digestion was a problem. Just seeing a pregnant woman triggered the memory of when my mom was pregnant with me, and she felt her enlarged belly was bad because it made her feel she looked ugly. So I decided my belly was bad also.

Another way to go is from the body centered therapy tradition. Look around your body, even run your hand around, and see if the feeling or image is coming from a certain location. This can free up your attention to realizing when you had this sensation in that particular place. Bodywork of the many types can also trigger memories, and I've used direct pressure to stimulate recovering a visual image of myself in the past. To do this, be prepared to have the trauma image flash in an out of consciousness so quickly it's easy to miss. Press sharply into the affected area then release. Keep repeating this until you can catch the image. I highly recommend seeing a Hendricks trained body centered therapist if you're stuck - they can see you do stuff with your body that you probably wouldn't spot on your own, which can lead back to the trauma.

It turns out that as we go through life, it's a lot like our consciousness is a pinball in a pinball game. As we get into a situation that reminds us of something painful, an image and or phrase from a past trauma pops up so quickly that we don't even notice them. Instead, we just instantly react and suppress to get away from the stimulus, just as if we'd hit one of the barriers that make a dinging sound and kicks the ball back into the center. With practice, you can learn to spot these images that drive your life to heal them. So how do you do this? Well, even knowing that this is going on will help you discover them for yourself. Another way is to get practice in spotting them. You can do this by using a GSR (Galvanic Skin

Response) meter, a sort of poor man's lie detector. It measures a change in electrical resistance of the skin as you work with emotionally charged material. With the help of a skilled operator (or yourself, with training), as these images flash into consciousness, the instrument needle will deflect momentarily. This gives you the practice to become aware of what just happened, and you can back up to try again until you catch it.

The Institute for Metapsychology in Menlo Park, California, teaches and works with clients using the GSR meter technique. Their power therapy TIR works well. But of particular interest to us is the way they can use the GSR meter to hunt out traumas that we're blocking from our conscious mind. I highly recommend their work. It's described in Dr. Frank Gerbode's book, *Beyond Psychology*. They also do an excellent job of describing how traumas connect together.

Another method is to go to a psychic to see if they can spot traumas for you. However, this is fraught with problems (not only fraud), and the best one I've ever worked with discovered one day by accident that roughly 10% of his clients would unconsciously feed him complete fantasy material, and he couldn't tell the difference. So beware of this approach - I highly recommend that anything from this approach be taken with a huge helping of suspicion. I recommend the GSR meter method instead.

Another technique is the old standby, silent breath meditation. But rather than trying to calm your mind, you use the stillness to allow material to come to the surface. Since you are not supposed to move, you can't distract yourself with the outside world. This can be a valuable aid to working, and some of my breakthroughs were during long meditation retreats. The short, 25 minute meditations have also given me priceless insights and experiences.

A sort of odd method to finding trauma involves using your dreams. I've gone to bed asking when the trauma that I was searching for happened, and I found that I'd wake up with a number from some part of the dream. This would be my age when the trauma happened. Another way to use dreams is to follow the series of feelings in the dream, and (usually) ignore the images and story line. You can find that often the dream had the same sequence of feelings as the real trauma, and bringing the feelings into consciousness also triggers the memory you've been searching for.

Occasionally I've found that I can use my own heart as a truth detector. If I'm having a difficulty in the present, and I happen to think about something from the past that is actually causing the problem, I'll get the sensation of my chest relaxing and opening up. I don't experience this very often, but it's pretty dramatic when I do.

One of the techniques that was so instrumental in my own healing was Holotropic Breathwork. I tend to think of it as dropping a rock on the psyche to smash through resistances, but it does that really well. The only major flaw their technique has is the lack of awareness that staying in your body during trauma is critical. Other than that, I highly recommend it. A variation I sometime use is to do hyperventilation breathing by myself for 15 minutes with music playing through headphones, to help me get into or explore specific issues. By far the best holotropic breathwork practitioners I've worked with are Sheelo and Amayo Bohm of North San Juan, California, and I highly recommend them.

Another extremely powerful technique is American Indian vision questing. I'm referring to the practice of going into the wilderness, sitting in one small area, and fasting for up to 4 days with the intention of healing or vision. This really works for me, and although I do this work solo, there are many competent leaders for this you might want to work with, at least at first. The only concern I might have with working with others is if they try and explain what your experience meant. Perhaps they'll be spot on, but perhaps not. So weigh it, just as you weigh what I have to say.

In a practical vein, say you have a decision you want to make. You know that you're not in the present with this, because you're feeling indecisive, or some other feeling, but not calm and at peace. What to do? Obviously, healing every trauma related to this, or changing your state of consciousness so the past no longer affects you emotionally (described later) is the best answer. However, there is another option. If you identify every feeling and thought about the issue, you'll get to temporary calm about it. This means that every trauma that feeds into this issue has to be given its say (metaphorically) before peace comes. And some of these, unfortunately, can be pretty obscure, and seemingly irrelevant. This may be something you can do for yourself, but when I did it, I used the help of somebody who could help me out.

Finally, you've read all of this forward and backward, and nothing has worked. Especially if it's a really awful feeling that you are dealing with, I can recommend one thing that's worked for several people, including myself. Just sit down, and let it wash over you in all its awfulness. In less than 30 minutes, it invariably reaches a crescendo, then suddenly 'breaks', and disappears. I don't know if it's gone forever (I rather doubt it), but at least it's out of your life for the time being. The hard part is just sitting down and not resisting it by doing something to distract yourself. The phrase "When the going gets tough, the tough go shopping" was probably invented for our normal response to this type of thing.

As an aside, it's possible to 'see' traumas and heal them directly while in the 'Spaciousness' peak state of consciousness. However, this is taught in the advanced class as it requires the therapist have the state. Basic WHH is limited to what people can do in 'average' consciousness.

THE WHH PROCESS—SECOND DEMONSTRATION & DISCUSSION

Again, we're going to do a demonstration of WHH. Now that you've read about the basic process, be thinking about how you're going to do it when we go into pairs on the next round.

Notes on Second Demonstration:

WOMB, BIRTH AND PRECELLULAR TRAUMA

Womb, birth, and precellular traumas often come up in our regression work as the origin of a 'trauma stack'. These types of traumas are extremely important to our work for several reasons. First, these types of traumas generally cause the biggest problems in ourselves and our clients, much more so than almost all post-birth traumas. Secondly, they also block peak states of consciousness (as described in our books *Peak States of Consciousness* Volumes 1 to 3). In this section, we're going to give you the basic information that you need to deal with these traumas. In class, we will be watching a video that *has in utero* micro-photographs that will help you to become familiar with the images that you and your clients will be seeing when regressed to this period. Many of the practice sessions you will be doing over the next four days will involve these types of traumas, and our intent is that repeated practice will help you feel comfortable in dealing with them. If you are interested, there are many good resources for information on this topic, for example from the Association for Pre- and Perinatal Psychology. Our advanced Whole-Hearted Healing training focuses on these types of traumas to a much greater depth.

What to expect—Womb memories

Fetal memories are quite different from typical traumatic memories. When you encounter one, after you heal you experience yourself in the womb as filled with bright white light and your body as very large, almost like you were a giant. This is the endpoint of a birth or earlier trauma - not only CPL, but a feeling of bright light inside the fetus, and the sensation that it is extremely large everywhere in the fetal body, larger than they are in the present. Keep the client healing until this endpoint occurs, then look for earlier related traumas.

Womb (and earlier) traumas only occur because of physical injury to your fetal body. This is because the fetus has a very different kind of consciousness than the adult self does (except in very rare cases). Many therapists don't realize this, and hence don't heal the issues in their clients fully because they don't treat the fetal injury. Thus, ideas like "The mother didn't want you and that was the reason for the trauma" are incorrect. Whether or not the mother wanted you is not experienced as a trauma to the fetus - it may not like it, but it doesn't 'stick'. However, if the mother's rejecting feelings happened *during* an injury, the fetus's feelings about how the mother felt would become part of the trauma. These injuries can include toxic foods ingested by the mother, smoking, electric shock, painful noise, and direct bodily injury from falling or sexual contact. So, even if you heal the emotional component, don't stop until you heal the physical pain. In cases of severe injury before birth the fetus appears darkened. Healing the injury causes the fetus to brighten and enlarge again. Be aware that the fetus can 'get large' in various parts of it's body, and not everywhere at once, as it heals different parts of the injury zone. Stay with it until the entire fetus is large and bright. The placenta is also part of the fetus, and must be included in the healing.

> **Example:** The first time Paula went into the womb, she had no idea that's where she was. She was in a warm place that was a uniform light gray. She felt she was her adult size, and wearing a cloak. She had recovered this memory on her own several times without any change. There were no emotions except a vague sadness. There was no physical pain until the therapist specifically told her to look for it. There were several injuries that came into her awareness. By focusing on the physical pain one at a time, she would then feel the associated emotions. The cloak turned out to be her placenta. She was very surprised to discover that her placenta was part of her and not part of her mother. It also had to be healed. At first, she thought her placenta was attacking her, because she felt it as a self-aware presence behind her fetal body.

> **Example:** A woman was involved with a man that physically abused her, yet she couldn't get herself to leave the situation. The feelings lead to a womb memory where her mother attempted an abortion and damaged the client as a fetus. The client saw how she was reproducing the feelings in the present from that womb trauma. After healing, the client no longer felt the overpowering need

to continue the relationship. Interestingly, she stayed in the relationship, but the physical abuse never happened again after that session.

It was a great surprise to me to discover that the fetus is entirely self aware and also thinking thoughts. Often, you'll experience the emotional copying you did from your mom at that time, but to really heal it you have to feel what YOU felt, both emotionally and physically, with the phrase your brain retained.

It's in these womb memories that you'll find the key to using your separate chakras. As fetuses, we watch our mother when she unconsciously uses them herself, and what she did at that moment to trigger their use is what we do to use our own. For example, my mom used her heart chakra when she bent over a patient to help them, and it's that sensation of bending over with a caring feeling that turns my own heart chakra on.

During my time in the womb, I stored many phrases in my head, constantly repeating over and over. 'Visually', they resemble sort of a small, wide, oval loop. If you turn your attention to them, and love them, they expand, you hear them, and they dissolve. This was one of the single most dramatic changes in my life. It's a bit hard to describe, but my thinking process changed from a sort of jangle (which I'd had my whole life, so I considered it normal) to a sort of smooth flow. It was remarkably wonderful!

In a similar way, feeling sensations are stored in the solar plexus region. They can be experienced as bubbles of various sizes, and dissolving them releases the trauma that formed them.

What to expect—Birth trauma

About 15% of the people I work with go to birth trauma in the first session. The birth trauma is actually composed of many traumas focused in individual injuries all over the body. When following a sequence of traumas to an origin at birth, we go to completion only at the particular injury site, not the entire birth experience. This is because it is virtually impossible to heal that much severe material all at once, for almost everyone.

> **Example:** I felt tremendous grief and loneliness radiating from my arms in the present while I was driving one day. I regressed myself back to the birth where these feelings arose. I was injured in the arms, shoulders, and neck during birth as I was pushed into the womb wall during contractions.

The single most helpful thing to speed the healing along is to really, really love yourself - to love yourself even while you feel tremendous pain. I've also found it can be very helpful to physically assume the position you had during that birth piece. The next most powerful thing is to feel deep love for your mother during the birth trauma, even though she is the cause of your agony. Trying to love your mother can also flush up resistance to doing so at that moment. Once that's healed, everything goes faster. (This is valid at anytime *in utero*, not just during birth.) Often what happens then is the mother and fetus then start to work together and the physical damage is minimized or even completely dissolved effortlessly.

The placenta has a significant place in the birth trauma. It is part of the fetus, and thus injury to it needs to be dealt with just like any injury in the main fetal body. We've found in a number of clients that issues can arise between the fetus and placenta, causing suicidal feelings or fear of separation later in life.

I recommend reading both Dr. Stanislav Grof's work on birth trauma and the coex system, for example *The Adventure of Self Discovery*, and Dr. Arthur Janov's later work on birth trauma, after he admitted such a thing was possible, such as *Imprints* or *The New Primal Scream*.

The 'No-Breath' technique for birth trauma

However, there is another technique that I've developed which I recommend using ONLY if the person is unable to face the birth experience completely. It goes as follows: just exhaust all the air out of your chest and belly. Compress your chest and don't breathe back in. In a little time you'll start to feel intense panic. This is often the feeling we resist when healing birth material, and this trick allows us to get in touch with it so we can heal it. This works on most people because during birth virtually every one of us felt intense panic from oxygen starvation due to the blood supply being cut off to the fetus during the contractions.

Dr. Adam Waisel came up with a better way to do this process. By simply holding your nose as you're working on the trauma, and breathing normally through the mouth, it acts as if you were holding your breath without the problem of traumatizing yourself in the present.

You'll find that the panic is actually stored in various separate locations in the body (see the discussion about 'holes' in day 2), and the technique tends to flush up the injury zones one at a time. After healing the first to arise, when you repeat the technique the next area feels panic, and so on. Although they're probably all present simultaneously, we probably notice them in sequence due to their relative severity. You know you've healed that particular birth injury when the panic you feel is completely gone from the injury—it can be hard to believe such a thing is possible, but it's a wonderful check on progress.

I also found in my own birth experience that my fetal self confused the experience of oxygen lack with being drugged with anesthesia during the birth. A simple technique for dealing with this is given in day 2.

The no-breath technique can be used to bring up birth memories at will. However, I **DON'T** recommend it in general unless you're willing to pay the potential consequences of activated but unfinished trauma in your life. You might have a major new emotional or physical problem suddenly show up. Even if you are used to intense inner work, I do not recommend this. Be warned! (Of course, this can also flush up trauma like drowning, which needs to be dealt with, but usually the intense experience of birth overshadows everything else.)

In an interesting historical note, the no breath technique is similar to the Essene practice of holding the neophyte under water until he nearly drowns in order to give him the experience of becoming 'reborn'. However, occasionally the neophyte would drown, a problem, which the no breath technique above doesn't suffer from.

What to expect—Egg and sperm memories

These memories can be quite unusual. For one thing, you can be now in two places at once, both as an egg and as a sperm. The egg in fact is created before your own mother is born from her mother, and experiences much of the traumas that she does, albeit in a sort of second hand way. When first encountering egg memories, one of the most striking things about it is that you feel like you still have a body, although you don't use your arms and legs, and that you feel like a very young version of your mother. Examples of egg trauma include compression damage during the mother's own birth, toxic chemical environment in the ovary, damage during ovulation and in the fallopian tube, and injury during conception.

The sperm is created later in the life cycle, comparatively shortly before conception. It also feels like a young version of the father. There is frequently a lot of trauma around being hit and injured by other sperm during its lifetime. Note that the sperm tail, experienced as extending from the upper back, is also part of the sperm, has rudimentary self-awareness, and must also be included in the healing.

Frequently, there is a huge degree of trauma around conception, when the sperm experiences 'death' during this experience. This, for most people, is an extremely traumatic memory. That sperm death is played out in relationships with men's fear of intimacy, a classic characteristic which is described so well in John Gray's *Men are from Mars, Women are from Venus*. Also, sperm tail injury as it separates from the back is common, as well as trauma around its death.

> **Example:** A 44 year old woman found herself irritated and wanting to leave the situation and companion she was with. She also had a feeling of pressure on her head. It was extremely difficult for her to stop moving around long enough to go inward to do WHH. The trauma turned out to be the sperm injuring its head during conception while it pushed into the covering of the egg. During the healing, the pain and anger just melted away.

When healing a client, if they describe that there is a painful experience that just abruptly ends in the midline of the body, you should suspect that it's either a sperm or egg memory. If the pain is on the right, it would be a sperm trauma, and if on the left, an egg trauma. However, occasionally we've had some clients where this orientation is reversed.

What to expect—Precellular memories

Occasionally, as you follow a trauma stack down to the origin, you'll find it goes back to before you existed as an egg or sperm. It turns out that each of the brains has an analog, or more correctly a structure that the later brains developed out of, inside the single cell. These memory images are visually quite strange, but some of the most significant and important traumas a person can experience often have their origin in these experiences. Thus, you might see such things as a quivering blob of jelly, a sort of palace, a kind of fountain, a ring that continues on forever, and all sorts of other structures and environments that we tend to try and put into terms we're familiar later in our lives. These traumas have major impact on our lives, because they occur so early and set us up for many later traumas - it's similar to how a small piece of falling snow can create a widening avalanche. We go into much more detail on precellular memories in the advanced WHH course.

These traumas are healed in just the same way as we always do - go into the 'body' at that time, and experience fully what happened until you feel large and bright.

Birth and pre-birth trauma are covered extensively in the advanced class. The material in this manual is adequate for most therapy situations, even though you may not understand exactly what the client is experiencing. Just do the WHH process as you normally would, and patiently wait until in the past they get to CPL, with internal light and a feeling of being very large.

Key Points:

- Womb trauma always involves a physical injury.

- The endpoint on a womb trauma is when the fetus feels very large and bright.

- Panic around not being able to breathe can be repressed by the client so they are unable to heal the trauma.

- The chain of traumas can lead to memories in the sperm or egg or even before the cell is constructed.

VIDEO—"JOURNEY INTO LIFE: THE TRIUMPH OF CREATION"

There are a number of important points we'll be covering while the video progresses. This film is particularly important to our work because it gives a visual perspective and scale that is the same as the OBE image that your clients will be encountering, even though most of them won't realize that's what they're actually seeing. I'll just list a few key points to help you recall them later:

•   The sperm is often hurt during the journey through the testes and fallopian tube.

•   The fertilized zygote is at extreme risk for death and crippling injury during the passage down the fallopian tube.

•   When the zygote reaches the womb, it feels like it's been shot out a roller coaster.

•   Major trauma can occur when the zygote has problems burrowing into the womb wall.

•   Normal hospital birth procedures almost always add unnecessary and major trauma to the baby

•   Caesarean section is even more traumatic than normal birth to the baby

(Incidentally, I also recommend the book by Lennart Nilsson called *A Child is Born* for excellent similar pictures.)

EXERCISE—PRACTICE WHH WITH A PARTNER

Although basic WHH was originally designed to be used by oneself for oneself, it works as well or even better with the assistance of a guide. Thus, for the remainder of the class we're going to generally work in pairs. What I'd like to stress about this is how useful it can be to be working with someone else, who can remind you that you're not in the present. For example, out of the blue two years ago I became very suicidal. I was convinced that my life was terrible, even though I wasn't working, had enough money and friends, a great place to live, and perfect weather. My mind went into overtime trying to find reasons in the present to explain why I felt like I did. By luck one day, I happened to touch my belly button, realize that the suicidal feelings were coming from there, and track it back to the moment when my umbilical cord was cut just after birth. All I can say is I'm glad I didn't kill myself first. This is a rather dramatic example, but you can imagine how it would help to have someone there to remind you that what you're experiencing isn't in the present. This can be particularly useful in job and personal relationships, where so much of what we feel has little or nothing to do with what's really going on.

For this exercise, pretend that you're working with a real client. Did you remember to record the issue and rate the SUDS? (If you really want to play, did you negotiate a price you'd charge for eliminating this issue?) You'll need to record the client's traumas, and if you don't finish in the time available, record the trauma image and the emotion and body sensation that you left your practice client at so that you can return to the trauma later. Then switch partners. You will each have about 30 minutes to work (i.e. 1 hour total), although this is the last activity for the day and you can stay until you want to quit.

In this class, we're going to get in as much practice time as possible. We've found that if we don't, the student's don't feel comfortable enough to use the process on clients.

Practice Session Notes:

Practice Session Notes (continued):

Quiz #1

1. Is the loving oneself process healing by itself? (i.e., if you client's pain went away when you had them do it, is their problem healed?)

2. What indicators do you use to know when a trauma is healed?

3. Do you always need a phrase with WHH?

4. Do you always need an image with WHH?

5. If you heal a trauma completely, and the client's presenting problem goes away, does this mean you are done with the trauma sequence?

6. What is a very simple way to help your client heal while they're in the trauma?

7.   If the client is doing WHH correctly, what is still the main mistake that clients still make?

8.   Do you expect the client to feel worse or better while they are doing WHH than the level of pain they had when they came in?

9.   What is a simple way to get an image when working with physical injury?

10. When is the best time to heal, i.e. when you are feeling really good, or when you're feeling really bad?

11. When you are in a conflict or problem with someone else, how do you tell if it's one of your traumas being activated?

12. If your client doesn't heal during the session, what does it mean? (3 possible reasons).

13.   What are the characteristics of a healed womb memory?

14.   Is the trauma 'stack' made up of similar memories or of similar feelings?

15.   One of the implications of this work is that blind people have visual images of trauma. Has this been found to be true?

16.   When might you use the no-breath technique?

17.   What is the key piece that helps the healing that is contained in the loving yourself technique (not the loving part)?

18.   Why does normal therapy involving remembering trauma not help the client? What does feeling large at the end of healing a womb trauma mean (or a trauma later in life for that matter)?

19. Can you be large in some areas and small in other areas when doing womb healing? If so, what would this mean?

20. What problems should you warn your clients of that might occur after a session of basic WHH?

21. Is loving yourself being conceited? Many clients think so. What would you say to them?

22. What is a helpful trick to get people to the correct phrase during a basic WHH session?

23. What does feeling a body sensation that stops at the vertical midline of the body often mean? i.e., only on the right or left side.

Day 2

THE TRIUNE BRAIN PLUS TWO: SELF IDENTITIES AND UNDERSTANDING WHY WHH WORKS

The Triune Brain

Eventually, if not sooner, Whole-Hearted Healing will bring up issues and experiences that have to do with what's really going on inside ourselves, especially around self-images and inner acceptance. In my own healing, it wasn't until I could recall my womb and birth memories that I could even understand why Whole-Hearted Healing really worked, let alone what these other experiences were about. In this section of the manual, we'll be describing the biological basis of the psyche.

We are actually composed of three separate primary biological brains, each possessing their own sense of self. The biology of this has been known since the 60's, and it's called the Papez-MacLean Triune Brain Theory. How this applies to our psyche is as follows:

The outer layer of the brain, the neocortex or primate brain, is the portion that thinks in sequences of words. This is our cognitive part, the mind, and 'it' perceives itself in the head. It 'thinks' in sequences of words. When we get the phrase in Whole-Hearted Healing, we are healing that portion of our being. Among other things, it is the part of us that can form judgments and do abstractions like mathematics. Its primary drive is to understand and secondarily to control. This brain is usually who we think we are.

The next layer down in the brain, the limbic system or mammalian brain, is our emotional consciousness, and 'it' thinks in sequences of emotions. It perceives itself in the chest, partially because this is the area of its primary biological responsibility. We often refer to this brain as the 'heart'. This portion of our being allows us to feel connected to others, positively or negatively, rather than experiencing people as if they were just objects, like stones. Its primary drive is to connect to others. By draining out the emotions when we heal with WHH, we are dealing with this brain. This brain is primarily the one that sees from the out-of-body perspective.

The final layer down is the body consciousness or reptilian brain, composed of the tissue at the base of our skulls, the spinal cord, and probably other distributed systems in the body as well. From a healer's perspective, this brain is not only primary biologically, but it's unhealed material dominates a person's life. This portion of ourselves gives us a sense of time, and it 'thinks' in gestalt sequences of internal body sensations. It experiences itself in the lower belly, since this is its area of major biological function. This is the brain that actually handles the movement of 'soul' pieces and the location of the out-of-body experience, as well as more mundane things like our sexuality. Its primary drive is to survive. We communicate with this brain when we do dowsing or muscle testing. This is the portion of ourselves we heal when we feel the body sensations and injuries in Whole-Hearted Healing.

There are two more distinct biological 'brains', but they can be considered sub-brains, because normally they're merged and indistinguishable from their respective 'parent' brain most of the time in average people. The first of these two is the solar plexus brain. It is intimately involved with the umbilical, placenta, and breathing. This is the brain is responsible for triggering the storage of traumatic memories with the out-of-body experience, which we feel as a tightening or contraction in the diaphragm, and also for the accessing of generational trauma into the body. Under normal circumstances, it is merged with the more fundamental body brain, described above. In people with severe psychiatric conditions, this brain is typically split from its primary brain and appears to be responsible for much of the patient's difficulties.

There are two more distinct self-aware brains that die off by birth - the placenta, which has its origins in a self-aware structure in the egg, and the sperm tail, which separates and dies during conception. These structures cannot be ignored while healing fetal, zygote, sperm, and egg trauma.

While doing WHH, we rarely need to know about the other sub-brain, the Buddha brain. It's also the most difficult to understand biological brain structure, and the last to evolve, located in the frontal lobes of the brain. We call it the 'Buddha brain' because clients often experience it as if it were a huge massive statue of Buddha overhead. This brain's center of self-awareness is actually a number of inches above the head. Actions of this brain create what clients describe as energy structures, connections, or shapes in the body that they sometimes see when they heal certain traumas. The literature generally lumps it in with its primary brain structure, the neocortex. Under normal circumstances it is merged with the mind brain.

Fusion of the brains

In the womb, the five brains are fused (merged) together, experiencing themselves as one organism. What finally put me on the right track to understanding this was a memory I recovered of a month or so before birth. My mom ate something that was poisonous to my fetal body. While dealing with this crisis, my mind broke from the fusion and experienced itself as a separate self. Later, during the birth trauma, all my brains split apart, and now there were three (sometimes five) separate senses of self. For humans and animals, this splitting is extremely common. Incidentally, the degree of fusion can vary from not being able to feel your emotions or body sensations to complete unity.

During the birth process, we typically become sort of amnesiac and lose this awareness of ourselves as a multiple brain system. As adults, each of our parts pretends that no one else is present, partly due to the tremendous level of trauma experienced around the split process. And each brain tends to view the world differently, depending on its primary purpose, capabilities, and subsequent traumas. Often, the brains work at cross purposes, for example when you find yourself sexually attracted (body) to someone you don't like (heart), and are confused about the situation (mind). In fact, they act just like a dysfunctional family, with the individual brains acting out different characters in the family. For example, one of the brains typically becomes dominant, another passive, and so on, just as in family dynamics. In my own case, I can recall the mind brain feeling left out when the body and heart merged, and so it 'played' the sound of my grandfather's voice stored in the mind that it knew would cause the other two brains to feel badly.

Complete internal fusion among the 5 brains is what most people are unconsciously seeking for in their outer world. Although some fortunate people have various types and degrees of fusion continuously since birth, or move in and out of it for various lengths of time routinely, the average person does not have any degree of fusion. The good news for the average person is that you can fuse at a moment's notice. The bad news is that few do. Although some average people may experience momentary fusion of some degree (one type of potential peak experience) due to external circumstances, to remain in a fusion state for these people is uncommon. For example, when making love with a particular partner, some people partially or fully fuse, occasionally causing their partner an unconscious permission to do likewise. This feels so awesome, they believe that there must be something special about the person they never want to give up! I also have some evidence that intentionally using your normal and peripheral vision simultaneously causes a degree of fusion between the mind and heart. What causes fusion and why certain types of spiritual or psychological practices may help some people is covered in our book, *Peak States of Consciousness*, Volume 1. But for the basic WHH process, you will find that your clients may move into one of the fusion states when doing WHH when you accidentally eliminate the traumas that reinforce the splitting.

Although there are a number of ways and degrees the 5 brains can fuse, I'll just mention three here. If you fuse just the head and heart and bring the body into the present, you stop reading in past emotional trauma and find yourself just in the present. This is called 'Aliveness' by Harville Hendrix in his book *Keeping the Love You Find*, and I suspect Native Americans call it 'The Beauty Way', while Christians call it an 'awareness of the immanent divine'. If you fuse the body and heart, men feel continuously happy, and women feel both happy and loving. When you fuse all five brains, you feel effortless and hollow. If you also heal the placental death trauma, you acquire the state of 'Wholeness'. Believe me, ordinary consciousness is like going to hell in comparison to fusion states! For a list of states with estimates of their occurrence in the general population, refer to the Institute of Peak States website at www.PeakStates.com.

For further reading on the three brains I suggest looking at Dr. Arthur Janov's, *The Anatomy of Mental Illness*. However, his work is flawed by a total rejection of any transpersonal phenomena. For a complete biological discussion, see Dr. Paul MacLean's *The Triune Brain in Evolution: Role in Paleocerebral Functions*. I recommend highly the books by Tom Brown Jr., in particular *Awakening Spirits*, which gives simple shamanic ways to temporarily accomplish fusion and other fundamental changes to the psyche. I came across these authors after I'd worked out this material myself, and it was a tremendous relief to know others had come to the same understanding following very different routes!

Self-identities

At the deepest level our resistances to internal fusion is projected into our outer relationships, as well as in self-images and inner projections. These projections are a 'best fit' to the underlying traumas that drive them, and particularly for birth trauma have tremendous impact. When you hit this sort of thing, healing the underlying trauma causes the projection to dissolve. In another example, in my own healing I found I projected out an 'overlay' of my dad on all men, and one of my mom on all women. Experiencing this is quite visually vivid, like some sort of video special effect. Again, all this is driven by trauma that should be tracked down and healed immediately.

Let's look more closely at this phenomenon of projection. When working with clients (or yourself), you can unexpectedly experience just such an internal projection of one brain on another. For example, during healing I've had people suddenly experience their body as the monster in the basement; the warrior goddess Diana; an Aztec god who rips hearts out. These particular projections had an overwhelming and mythic quality to them because to the head and heart, the body consciousness feels like a god, which makes sense from a biological perspective since the body is primary.

Each brain also holds unconscious self-identities, again driven by trauma. Some interesting ones I've come across; the heart consciousness unconsciously pretending it was Jesus on the cross, the body consciousness pretending it was it's father, the brain experiencing itself as a crystal palace, an elaboration of the baby milk bottle. I believe in virtually everyone the heart consciousness primarily identifies itself as the mother, and the other brains also retain that projection of the emotions. This is why spotting mother copies can be so difficult.

Shutting the brains off

In a rare client, you can find that the brains have turned themselves 'off', individually or in groups. (I discuss this in more depth in the section about spiritual emergencies.) However, they lose the abilities that are primary to those shut down brains. For example, turning off the body and emotional consciousness results in samahdi, with its sense of peace, timelessness, and lack of almost any need to breathe. (The two shut down brains no longer need the oxygen they normally require for their chemically based 'thinking' processes.) Or shutting down the mind and heart results in an experience of the 'Pearl Beyond Price' from Sufi tradition, with its lack of body boundaries and fullness in the belly. Shutting down the emotional consciousness eliminates any feeling that others are people and not just objects. I wouldn't be surprised if this was the origin of sociopathic personalities, if done early enough under enough trauma.

Generally, the client finds life is internally easier without the given brain present (less internal arguing), except that their outer life suffers - for example, they find they can't make decisions if the mind shuts down, and so on. This condition can generally be reversed if they decide to want the quality of the brain that has disappeared out of their life.

Applying the triune brain model to understanding how basic WHH works

With an understanding of the internal dynamics of the human brain, we can now understand how basic WHH works. When we do WHH, we feel the body sensations (the reptilian brain), the emotions (the mammalian brain), and the phrase (the primate brain). By experiencing all three of these parts of ourselves, we completely heal the trauma we are working on. And in fact, the basic WHH process is actually forcing a temporary fusion of the three brains in that past moment of trauma.

The endpoint of healing a trauma occurs when the client feels "CPL" - calm, peace, and lightness. Up to now, I've just told you this is the case, but now you can understand why. CPL is the characteristic of the client actually being in the present, no longer in the traumatic past. As you've read, this occurs when the heart and mind fuse together. When a client is done using WHH, they'll be CPL for various lengths of time, from just seconds to days, until the brains un-fused. As you can expect, some of your clients will go into even better states, for example they might say they "feel whole" for the first time in their lives. But we want at least CPL as an endpoint to a client's healing. (And in fact, **all** trauma healing therapies should have this same endpoint of CPL, they just don't realize its importance.)

This idea of forcing a fusion by using basic WHH can be extended. Imagine for a moment that the three brains are already induced into fusion at the moment of trauma. As long as they stay in body, one finds that healing the trauma becomes fast, easy, and sometimes completely painless (depending on your degree of fusion)! It's only an artifact of 'normal' consciousness that causes such slow healing in ourselves. In fact, this is the basis of one of the advanced WHH healing techniques, where we induce fusion into the client as they're working. Unfortunately, unless you get outside assistance in becoming fused, or are lucky enough to have already been fused, this option is not available to you and you're forced to use the basic WHH approach, or "brute force and ignorance" or "the snail method" as we like to call it.

Interestingly enough at this point in my work with people I can monitor in someone else's body how well the five brains are allowing themselves to fuse. At least some measure of fusion, however small, seems to be required to heal traumas. In fact, the 'loving yourself' process discussed earlier also tends to help the fusion process along. We hope to eventually discover better methods to accomplish this from average consciousness to improve the Whole-Hearted Healing procedure.

A final note: There is more to the WHH process than an understanding of the triune brain can explain. WHH actually involves interactions with the Creator and with 'Gaia'. These connections are why 'staying with a trauma' changes what happened. Especially in womb trauma, the client unknowingly uses Regenerative Healing during the process. However, this is beyond the scope of this manual. If you're interested in understanding more about this, see our *Peak States of Consciousness, Volume 2: Acquiring Extraordinary Spiritual and Shamanic States.*

Key Points:

- There are three main brains and two sub brains in the human body.

- Basic WHH forces a fusion of the brains to create healing

- The brains hold self images of themselves

- The endpoint of trauma healing, calm peace and lightness (CPL), is a usually temporary fusion of head and heart.

UNUSUAL PHENOMENA DURING HEALING AND WHAT TO DO

What to expect—Healers 'picking up the clients problem'

As mentioned earlier, occasionally you will run into a certain type of trauma where the Whole-Hearted Healing technique will not drain away the emotion no matter how long you work at it. This occurs because the emotion is not actually your own, but rather a 'copy' of someone else's emotion who was present during the trauma. You 'copy' by leaving your body and moving your viewpoint into the other person's chest. Although most people quit doing this fairly early in life, a significant number of people, especially in the healing professions, tend to continue this practice unconsciously. Unfortunately, it does not help the client and is harmful to the healer, in spite of what some healers think.

How does this show up in your practice? Generally, during or after a session you feel like you now have the same symptom of the client, for example their sore knee, or deep sadness. Doing this to yourself is not related to the client's symptom—it's related to the client's emotion just being an exact match to emotions your mom had *in utero*. That's why you will do it with some clients, and not others.

We STRONGLY suggest that you eliminate any tendency to do this! We suggest you heal this problem in the WHH training, or soon after. How to do this? Try and recall a time that this actually happened. If you can't, you'll just have to wait till you spot yourself picking up the client's problem during a session sometime in the future. Now, you have both the clients trigger emotion (the one that you got from them), and your own 'hidden' emotion that was covered by the copy. This hidden emotion is the trigger feeling that pushes you to do the copying. Now, use Whole-Hearted Healing to follow the trigger feeling back to its source, usually birth and womb trauma. Generally, you might expect that your mom had the client's emotion during the core trauma, but not always - it's your trigger feeling that's the key here. Regardless, you get rid of the copy by becoming aware of what your own body actually felt emotionally at the moment you copied. As you do, the copied emotion dissolves, often with the sensation of it spreading and flying away from your body.

What to expect—Buddha brain structures

You might be working on a client, when suddenly they might say they see a container or tube or something that looks like an 'alien implant' inside their body just like in Star Trek. Or, there is pain in two parts of the body that don't have really any physical connection, especially pain of a pulling type, like two places are being pulled together by a cord. If you even suspect this might be the case, WHH will eventually cause it to disappear once you find the trauma that caused it. However, you can speed this process up by having the client love themselves at a place above their heads! As you'll read about later, these structures are created by the sub-brain we call the Buddha brain, which in normal people has its center of awareness centered above the head. That's why it speeds things up to focus love on it there.

What to expect—Holes

Occasionally after healing a trauma, or by using some other therapy, you are left with a distinct feeling of lack, deficiency, and emptiness. What has happened is that you have removed the defenses to feeling a 'hole'. Often, you will actually see it as a black, seemingly bottomless cavity whose opening is flush with the surface of your body. A rim of a somewhat different shade encircles the perimeter. Every human body has a network of holes in it. They are created during physical trauma to your body, with the majority of large holes coming from birth.

Healing a hole you can see is done by putting 'yourself' into it, enduring the awful feeling of lack, until the image of when the damage occurred comes to awareness. You then go ahead and heal the trauma in the usual manner. As you feel the physical pain, you can see the hole becoming lighter and lighter as it fills in, with the rim dissolving last. Believe me, when you see a hole, the last thing you want to do is go near it, but this is exactly what you must do, and immediately. I put off healing the first hole I found, losing my ability to see it in minutes. It took 5 years before I could find it again.

If you can't see the hole, the feeling of lack typically feels like it is coming from everywhere. Running your hand around your body will help you to localize the sensation to a specific spot. Then focus yourself as much as possible into the lack, and see if the traumatic memory of the injury surfaces. If nothing seems to be coming up, try pressing your fingers into that area. This usually triggers the out-of-body image into consciousness. In fact, during the healing of the hole, we've found that using direct pressure on the hole area can allow healing for some people that can't do it any other way.

> **Example:** Paula notes that for her there is almost always a point in the healing when it feels like "this hole will never go away". This means she's about 2/3 to 3/4 of the way through healing the hole. It's like clockwork for her, and now she knows to expect this feeling.

A tremendous amount of our behavior and feelings is driven by a need to block our awareness of the holes. In fact, if you scan your body, when you locate any strong feeling at a specific location, you can be pretty confident that a hole is located at that spot. We try and cover them and fill them in all sorts of bizarre ways. For example, I found myself literally addicted to a woman who reminded me (totally without my awareness) of my mother. During a long meditation, I felt my definition of myself as a person in relationship with her dissolve. This was my primary defense to this particular hole, one in the center of my chest. The next thing that happened was that a body worker noticed that my chest stuck out like the prow of a boat. This was my final line of defense, as I unconsciously tried to contract my body in that area, to give me physical sensations to counteract the sense of lack and emptiness of the hole.

I suspect that much of our resistance to healing certain traumas is caused by trying to keep up our defenses to our holes. At a very deep level, I think we usually prefer feeling painful emotions to feeling the terrible emptiness of the holes. For an interesting view on the phenomena of holes, I refer you to the writings of A. H. Almaas, in *Diamond Heart, Book 1*. (However, I disagree with a lot of his material.) I do recommend *Seawork: Radical Tissue Transformation* by Dr. Cory Sea, which gives another way to work with this phenomena. More on holes will be covered in the advanced WHH class.

What to expect—Past lives

When following down a sequence of traumas, you might find that you go so far as to end up in another lifetime! Or, through other work, you may have gotten in touch with such a past life trauma. You will recognize yourself, even though you have a completely different body and personality, and you will often recognize others you know in this lifetime in that past traumatic situation. It turns out that we heal them in exactly the same way as a trauma in this lifetime. One of the more controversial discoveries we've made in the last few years was to find that encountering a past life memory is *not* the core of the issue. Clients access past life material to escape a similar sensation in this lifetime. You can choose to heal the past life memory or not, but once the pressure is handled from the past life, perhaps for practice, the trauma in this lifetime needs to be healed.

For the typical person, there are so many lifetimes that trying to heal them all is completely pointless. We access those moments simply because those particular past life traumas have a similar sensation to the ones in this lifetime.

About 1% or 2% of the people I've worked with find themselves in a past life the first time we work together, but with more healing work the other people start finding this stuff. However, beware! I discovered that about 3% of the people I work with the first time come up with fake past life stuff, especially folks who are into new age philosophy. It tends to be delusional, as in seeing Christ on the cross, being in Atlantis, missing out in a group ascension to heaven, etc. Why am I so sure it's delusional?

Because they don't heal when dealing with this, but when I have them stay in their own lifetimes with the feeling, they do heal, and they realize the past life was a fake.

What to expect—Generational traumas

Especially while working with birth or womb trauma, or with so-called 'genetic' or inherited problems, you will often find that the source of the problem is coming from trauma that occurred in your past generations. Unlike past lives where you can recognize yourself, you will be aware that the individual being traumatized in the past is not yourself. There is a sensation of seeing layers of people with the same problem stretching back through time. Notice that these traumas can occur after the next generation is born; it is not passed along only in the womb.

How can you recognize the client's problem is coming from a generational trauma, and not from some trauma in their own lifetime? Generational traumas always feel very personal in the present, not just in the regression, as if it were about you personally, not just a feeling or sensation. Doing a history on the client to see if a parent or grandparent had the same problem is usually pretty conclusive, and should be kept in mind in any WHH healing session as a possible cause. Occasionally, if nothing else has worked, I'll try healing generational influences just in case. Some clients can feel that the problem is coming from a direction that's usually angled forward in the upper right or upper left. They also, once the nature of the problem is explained, can often feel that it's from some ancestor, at first usually a parent. These are the easy clients to work with!

Generational traumas are present in both the sperm and egg from the parents, and never leave as the fetus grows into an adult. Experientially, they are found in various locations inside the body. These generational traumas cause some traumas to feel 'personal', rather than impersonal. For example, an 'impersonal' trauma can be compared to a child playing who scrapes or bruises himself, but thinks nothing of it other than to note the sting or ache as he continues to play. Using the same example, a 'personal' trauma might be the same event where the child notices the injury but feels like it says something about themselves, like "I'm always clumsy" and so on. The first example is just about a pain that happened - the second example is about how we feel the pain has something to do with us and who we are.

Many traumas are nearly impossible to heal because they are associated with, or even caused by, these generational traumas. The difficult feeling or pain can be completely overshadowed by how 'personal' the trauma feels - for example, we may feel the experience is actually saying what a 'bad' person we are. However, healing the generational trauma *first* can make an otherwise torturous experience with WHH feel almost trivial in comparison.

> **Example:** I was working on a trauma involving shame. It was so personally disturbing that I couldn't get in body to heal. This went on for weeks. Finally, it occurred to me that it did feel very personal. With that thought, I flashed to my Grandfather during the depression, where he was feeling the shame of not being able to provide for his family. Healing that took only a few minutes (it was his pain, not mine). Returning to my shame trauma, I found that it no longer felt personal - the shame was just another feeling like any other feeling. The healing only took a couple more minutes.

At birth, a non-physical layer is acquired by the birthing baby from the mother. This layer gives us the sensation of having skin, and also makes events that happen to us feel personal, in the same way that generational trauma do. This is described in a later section on the 'shell'.

You can have your client access these generational traumas by regressing them to an *in utero* time when the generational trauma was a problem that caused injury. Once at the right time, the client can usually 'see' generation after generation going back into the past with the same issue. It looks like a string of people, or a deck of cards with people's images going upwards and to the right. Have them go as far as it takes to get to the first one, heal it, and then the most amazing thing happens - the client can watch the problem dissolve in generation after generation at about a 5 second/ generation rate as the change comes forward into the present. (When healing an ancestor, note that you don't have to heal all of their problems, just the trauma that was apparent when you first tracked the problem to them.)

How does one tell a generational trauma from a past life trauma? First of all, a generational trauma makes the trauma you're working on feel personal - and so it's hard to face and heal. Past lives, on the other hand, feel impersonal, and hence much easier to heal. Of course, you might have a generational trauma from 'you' in a past life - uncommon, but we've seen it occur.

Another very successful therapy for these problems is TAT, described later in this course. I recommend using TAT for this problem first, as it is generally the fastest and simplest method for generational trauma (if TAT will work for your client).

It is possible to eliminate all generational traumas at once. This is covered in the advanced WHH training. Typically there are well over a hundred of them. Clients who have done this all note that their hearing gets much more sensitive, as a sort of body level background murmur vanishes. It is also possible to eliminate the shell, which makes the skin layer feel like it no longer exists. Again, this is covered in the advanced WHH training.

What to expect—Soul pieces

While working on yourself, you might experience what looks like a person or a dark cloud of smoke suddenly leaving your body. Or while helping someone else heal, you might leave the session and continue to feel terrible, yet know that you didn't have one of your own traumas activated. Or you or a client is experiencing 'possession', channeling, or severe mental illness. To understand what happened and what to do about it, you need to have some shamanic background along with more conventional experience.

As a hypothesis, assume that your sense of 'I', of consciousness, is composed of a non-physical 'material' that is a small portion of the Creator itself. Shamans call this stuff 'soul'. During a few certain traumas, the pain is so bad that you actually eject a piece of yourself along with the emotional memory of what happened out of your body area, and it wanders around loose. In the shamanic tradition, this is called soul loss. If a shaman brings yours back to you, they call it soul retrieval. If you've got somebody else's, this is called soul stealing. In Christian terms, these soul pieces would probably be called entities or angels, depending on the emotional tone of the trauma that formed the piece. Visually, at one level of consciousness they look like the people at the instant they were formed, and at another they look like a little cloud of smoke from a pipe. The only book I can recommend in this area is a great one by Sandra Ingerman called *Soul Retrieval*.

When doing healing on a client, they might tell you that they have a terrible lacking feeling, even though you can verify that the trauma has been healed. If the client waits up to three days, the 'lack' feeling will suddenly disappear with a pop as the missing soul piece eventually returns. Since we don't want our clients to walk out of our office with this feeling, here is a trick to bring the soul piece back. Have them sing (or hum or chant) the first song that pops in their head. This song, often one they haven't thought of in years, is related to the missing soul piece. Generally between the first and third time through, the soul piece will return with a 'popping' sensation and the client's feeling of lack will suddenly vanish.

These soul pieces are the origin of the voices in the head people experience in severe mental illness, or during channeling. One of my teachers told me that holding on to others' soul pieces is the root cause for all serious mental illness, and I suspect he may be right. The good news is soul pieces don't have us, we have them! Contrary to what the movies and most healers say about this, no matter how bad it is, even if it drives us crazy or causes us to harm people, we're hanging on to them, they're not hanging on to us. It turns out that the reason is buried in womb and birth trauma, which is why nobody knows it. During these experiences, which the fetus feels are life threatening, our mothers felt a variety of feelings, good or bad. Our bodies associate survival with the feeling of having external emotions (our mother's) surrounding us, which is what soul pieces feel like. We literally believe at an unconscious level that our survival depends on surrounding ourselves with those feelings. For example, one woman found multiple layers when she healed the birth trauma piece, and found an even earlier trauma that happened when her mom fell down the stairs, landed on her very pregnant belly, and desperately wanted her husband to help her.

So, what to do? If you're channeling, you can track back to the source trauma by feeling how you feel when you call the soul piece up. If you're like most of us, you're doing your damnedest not to hear any voices. For you, look to your outer relationships. If you're physically attracted to a certain type of person who usually feels a certain way (as I was to angry women), you might suspect birth and womb trauma. Not only do we surround ourselves with a soul piece of a certain feeling, we add to the mess by finding people who tend to have that feeling we think we need to survive. Healing this has the added benefit of eliminating two problems at once!

I'll finish by mentioning something that might not occur to you to heal. My mom had many of positive feelings during birth too, and when I broke the connection between survival and these nice feelings, I felt myself throw off a whole bunch of positive feeling soul pieces, which psychics in the new age circuit often call 'angels'. This sensation was unexpected enough, but the big surprise was that the noise in my head dropped dramatically, just as if someone had turned off the background air conditioning in a building, or turned down the tape hiss on a stereo. A wonderful experience!

The advanced WHH class specifically goes into healing this problem as part of the course work. We call the process the 'Silent Mind Technique'. It's required because of the inadvertent risk of soul stealing when 'merging' with clients. We've also recently developed a new technique that eliminates all soul stealing simultaneously.

What to expect—Chakras and Meridians

To our surprise, these so called energy centers described in Hindu spiritual texts actually exist, and can cause unusual problems in our clients. In normal people, the chakras are located physically separated, although in people who have them developed fully, they are merged into a disk located near the solar plexus. In this class, we'll just cover the typical person's case.

The chakras tend to work differently, but when large amounts of energy is flowing out of them, it will feel just like water is streaming out of the body at their locations, almost like a hose is connected inside ourselves pointing outward. We unconsciously use the chakras by having triggers that we've learned from watching our mother *in utero* unconsciously use hers. Thus, to control our own, we simply feel whatever state our mom was in when she used hers. For example, my own mother was a nurse, and when she leaned over a client with a loving feeling, her heart chakra would open and send out energy. She would open her crown chakra during sex, and so on with different triggers for the others. Like our mother, we generally use them unconsciously, which is where the potential problems lie.

Let's start with the crown chakra. It's located at the top of the head, and if it opens spontaneously it may feel like a gigantic hand is pressing down on the head, to the point of pain. The pressure location occurs at trauma points that block the chakra's "energy flow" - as each trauma is healed, the pressure shows up at the next one down until there is no longer a sense of pressure from the flow. Thus, treatment is to heal the blocking traumas, but the other option is to have the client turn off the chakra. In this second case, have the client notice what feeling/emotion/sensation is the trigger, and have them stop it. Clearly that's unreliable in moments of stress or forgetfulness, so unblocking the chakra is preferable.

Using the third eye chakra is particularly interesting, and can be very disturbing to some people. If used by itself, it looks like X-ray vision, in photonegative shades of gray. Integrated properly with the rest of the body's systems, it gives the potential to see behind things, which can be very disturbing to some people. Follow the same guidelines as above.

The heart chakra is particularly interesting from a clinical view. In several clients, the ability to use the heart chakra was blocked by a 'hole' in the chest, which also gave them addictive problems - alcohol, relationships, etc. Unfortunately, healing the chest hole can be excruciatingly painful, as it is often formed while the fetus is being squashed through the birth canal during birth.

The solar plexus chakra is a major problem area for many people. At this time, we believe that the damage to this area is due to using our solar plexus to reach out and grab onto things, or push them away. This can damage us severely with the sensation of our diaphragm is being ripped out or apart as we try and push or pull things *in utero* that are just not going to move.

Again, in a normal person, the separate chakras are anchored into the meridian 'webbing' in a body. If they're not anchored correctly into the meridian webbing, the person acts either completely physically drained and tired, or so energized they can't quit moving. When the whole system is working correctly (or at least as correctly as we've figured out how to do so far), we've found that the typical person only uses three or four hours of sleep a day to feel fully rested.

This material is beyond the scope of the class, but you should know it exists. We work with this material in much more depth in the advanced WHH training.

What to expect—Anesthesia and other drugs

When a client issue leads to a trauma involving anesthesia, you can find it difficult to heal. Often, this type of trauma occurs during birth, and an already painful and difficult experience becomes nearly unmanageable. The client will often feel numb, paralyzed, stupid, unfeeling, and cold. Reassurance and a blanket to keep them from being chilled helps. Generally, you can wait out this type of trauma, and the anesthesia experience will pass, but often very slowly. We found by experiment that a 'cranial hold' technique where you massage the back of the neck, just under the large bump at the top of the spine, and simultaneously massage the bony area at the front of both temples at the sides of the forehead will often expedite the release of the experience. This massage technique also works on other types of drug overdoses, such as from anti-psychotic medication.

However, the client generally is overdosed with the anesthesia, and it is stored in the body, especially in the diaphragm region. Getting this out of the body generally requires the use of a breathwork technique involving hyperventilation. I recommend the use of Grof's Holotropic breathwork or Hendricks breathwork technique. The client should be warned that the chemical will come out of the skin and breath, and in fact the client can just reek of the smell, saturating the clothing. With more breathwork experiences, other anesthesia experiences will release their particular chemical. This release can be speeded by having the client love the solar plexus / diaphragm area, as if it were a child still holding a grudge, and in the case of birth anesthesia, love the mother also. Doing basic WHH on these types of traumas doesn't eliminate the stored chemicals in my experience. I don't know if leaving them in the body is harmless or not, but just in case I'd recommend the hyperventilation techniques to help get rid of it.

I've also found that at least one psychoactive medication blocks the WHH process. It's called desipramine and it is specifically designed to block the client's access to traumatic feelings. Matt Fox reports that "Zanex also blocks WHH and also appears to effect EFT. Klonopin also blocks WHH, and it takes roughly 4 to 6 weeks after the drug is discontinued before WHH works normally." I suspect others exist too, but amazingly enough most drugs don't seem to block the healing.

Key Points:

- Basic WHH will often bring up unusual experiences in your clients, and reassuring them it's normal will help them.

- Holes are caused by physical injury, and feel like a deficient emptiness.

- Soul loss will cause your client to have a feeling of lack or something missing.

- Past lives always lead to trauma in this life. Healing a past life is not adequate to heal the client's issue.

- Generational traumas should always be checked for in a client's history.

- Anesthesia trauma can be healed with WHH, and a particular body therapy assists.

INCREASING YOUR SKILL:
MOVING AWAY FROM THE ROTE WHH PATTERN

The trauma 'stack' isn't always straightforward

In the short guide to the process, I emphasize going into the past traumas as if they were plates on a stack. Generally, we want to go to the original, 'core' trauma as fast as possible and heal that because when we do, we find that the other traumas later in time just dissolve without any additional attention. Although this is generally true, there is an exception – we sometimes find ourselves 'stuck' in a trauma, and have to heal it either partially or fully to be able to move earlier in the stack. Also, some stacks have more than one traumatic root, and require us to go earlier to several different origins.

Another interesting variation on this theme are a few clients who echo back and forth between an early and a later trauma. I've tried forcing them to stay in the earlier one, and this has worked OK, but it's generally more productive and honors their own intuitive healing sense to go with the back and forth flow. Generally this occurs because there is significant physical injury in both the earlier and later trauma. However, beware of a few clients who just go to a number of traumas, as they are generally using that to avoid feeling the pain of any one of them (like they were channel surfing on TV).

Another simplification I've made to the real process is to suggest that there is a single sensation that links all the traumas through time together. Although this is often the case, sometimes the theme changes due to a trauma associating a new theme to an older one. When going down the 'stack' of traumas, you might find the theme shifting due to this. The client will recognize how they are connected, and the process will continue in the same automatic fashion as it always did. (When I talk about themes, I mean theme's of body sensations, NOT storyline or emotional trigger objects such as spiders or test situations. Students often confuse the two, but the storyline or trigger is essentially irrelevant, contrary to our analytical thinking. If you're interested, I suggest reading about the TIR process as it covers the ways that traumas connect in much more detail.)

Using variations on the basic technique to access and heal trauma

You'll find that you might need to use a variety of techniques to access and ease healing of some clients, or some particular issues. These are used to speed the healing, find the images, identify and locate the traumas, and facilitate getting into the body. Later, I'll be covering using WHH with other power therapies, but for now there are several simple things you can do:

- Use the loving yourself technique (first choice)

- Use the ball of white light technique

- Sing a song, both for soul return and to relax the body

- Use hyperventilation

- Run your hand over your body to locate the physical injury that is the source of the painful emotion.

- Use psychological reversal correction (such as collarbone breathing, rubbing the sore spot, or tapping the karate chop point from EFT) from energy therapies to ease resistance.

- If the trauma is not moving quickly, it's often the exact wording of the phrase that's the problem. Try having the client keep repeating whatever phrase they've gotten, and like doing stream of consciousness work, see if it morphs into the exactly correct phrase.

- If the emotion or pain is localized in one location, allow it to expand into the whole body. This can sometimes be accomplished by actually trying to shrink it, and then letting it rebound outward into the entire being. When it's in the entire body, the healing is drastically increased in speed.

Some hints when using WHH

- If a trauma doesn't move there is usually a bigger, more painful one underneath it.

- Positive emotions have to be healed as well as painful ones—CPL is the endpoint (the only exception is happiness, as this is actually a peak state, but continue on to CPL anyway).

- When healing pain, get in the position of maximum pain and generally an image will come.

- Or, use a pressure technique on the area of injury to induce the image. Likewise, if you can sense an emotion in one particular location, press there. To do this, have the client ready to see the image flash in and out of awareness when you first briefly press into the area. Repeat as often as needed to get it into awareness.

- For trauma in the past that won't release: find the painful spots in the injured area, and maintain pressure on them, one by one, until the pain fades away while staying in the past. This triggers aspects of the trauma into awareness.

- In some traumas, when you are done with your side of the issue, it can be important to heal the other person involved (An example is rape trauma). This is outside the scope of the class at this time.

- Things always seem worse just before a breakthrough.

- Generally, the most painful piece of work is always the current one you're working on no matter how tough the earlier one's were.

- When things are healed it is difficult to remember how painful it was before the healing.

- Your success healing something is often lost from awareness when other issues start coming up.

- After healing an issue, there is a gap of seconds to days before the next piece to be healed comes to consciousness and becomes 'your big issue' that you believe has to be dealt with to be happy.

Changing the past

One of the most surprising and probably controversial parts of our work involves the nature of time itself. In our culture, our usual model is that the past is fixed, and the future has yet to be determined, and our awareness is in the present. This turns out to be completely wrong. For the moment, you'll have to take on faith that the way time actually works is that the past, present, and future that we are familiar with have already happened. Thus, if you were to 'visit' yourself in the past, that person would be experiencing that moment in the past as their present. Or someone 200 years ago, likewise they are in their 'present' moment. This also means that if you move forward in time, such as is described by Hank Wesselman in *Spiritwalker*, you would be in the 'present' there. However, it isn't a static universe - it's constantly changing, and the future can interact with the past to change the past. The typical person in our culture changes their own future, typically in small ways, about 3 times a year. Thus, although to a great extent it feels a bit like a clockwork universe, change (at a level outside of time itself) can happen, and so predestination isn't necessarily the case. To put it in another way, your future (for example) has already happened - but sometimes it can be changed.

This bit of information isn't totally necessary for you to know or believe, but it can show up with clients doing WHH in the following way. It turns out that the WHH process is actually changing the past, and in fact when the core trauma is eliminated, the changes move forward in time changing the 'future'. Thus, occasionally, when doing a really profound core trauma, you might find the client suddenly and spontaneously has a new set of memories occur. This phenomenon can also occur when using Zivorad Slavinski's DP-3 process.

> **Example:** For example, one client recalled an episode where he was hit by a teacher when he was a small boy. After this was healed, he found himself, quite involuntarily and without any forethought reaching out to the teacher in a loving way, something that had not happened in the 'previous' past, and the whole interaction was different.

There is another important point about all this. When you do WHH on a past trauma, you find that the emotional, physical, and mental content of the trauma vanish. We tend to think this is because we've "erased the memory", but this is *not* the case. Instead, we've gone back in time and changed what happened! (A real application of "raising ourselves by our own bootstraps".) This principle becomes glaringly obvious when we heal pre-birth trauma. As you recall, these traumas always involve injury. After you get to CPL with the trauma, the client reports there is no injury or any other issue left. Yet, they can still regress to that moment in time and re-experience what caused the damage, be it an attempted abortion, toxic chemicals, ripped placental lining, or what have you - but it's re-experienced *without* any injury to the fetal body. This occurs because the client in the past experiences the trauma but is healing any damage as it occurs, effortlessly. This is an application of the Regenerative Healing process described in day 4, but one that is not obvious to clients. They just accept that this is the way the WHH therapy works.

> **Example:** A woman in her fifties had accidentally been left un-anesthetized during electroshock therapy. By going over the trauma a number of times, all the pain and discomfort eventually disappeared, as it should with the WHH therapy. As she was in an advanced state of consciousness in the present, she could clearly 'see' how her body in the past was handling the electroshock to keep it from causing any injury to herself.

However, there are ways to change the past that you shouldn't try. This problem occurs in particular with past life memories. When you do a past life memory, there is enough separation between the self in the present and the self in the past that they can interact - and you might find your client trying to change the past by having the person in the past do something differently. THIS IS A BAD IDEA for several reasons. First, the old trauma will still is a problem for you. That won't change. Second, since you've got traumatic pain around the situation, you will tend to just make matters worse—a bit like you don't want to get advice on suicidal feelings from someone who feels suicidal themselves. Third, and although this sounds really delusional, remember the golden rule—would you like someone in your future suddenly becoming present and giving you bad advice, advice you'd feel must be good since they were obviously a 'disembodied spirit'?

> **Example:** A woman was working on an issue and it lead her to recalling a past life memory of being burned to death. Rather than doing WHH on it, she decided to avoid experiencing the pain by trying to outsmart the situation by moving earlier in time, and managed to communicate with herself in that lifetime. She then got the past life self to avoid the sequence of events that originally lead to the burning by having her earlier lifetime poison herself! However, her symptoms in the present didn't change (as we've said, past life trauma hides trauma in this lifetime). She didn't make progress on her issue until she went back, went to the original past life burn injury (yes, she could still access it even though there was a 'new' lifetime), did WHH on it, then proceeded to find the earlier trauma in this lifetime that was responsible for her issue.

I'll just emphasize this point one more time. DO NOT TRY AND CHANGE THE PAST. We're often so desperate to have the past be different than it was that we actually can become delusional about the issue. This is a real problem! Instead, heal the past with WHH or some other therapy so that you don't need to change what happened - and if it changes spontaneously, that's no problem. Just be sure that it was spontaneous, and that the client isn't sneakily trying to avoid the pain of the past.

WHH ON PHYSICAL ISSUES

WHH and other power therapies will often heal physical problems, problems that one might not consider possible to heal without medical procedures. (If you weren't aware of this, we refer you to the EFT website for the huge variety of conditions that have responded to these types of therapies.)

However, physical issues are generally not as straightforward as emotional ones to heal. The mechanisms that create the physical illness are often only indirectly related to trauma, and several types of mechanisms exist. One of the primary purposes of the Institute is to search out the mechanisms and underlying traumatic causes to a variety of serious illnesses. Below we'll list some of these mechanisms and give examples.

Symptoms directly related to trauma

In this class of illnesses, the cause is a trauma whose emotional tone in the past is the same as the emotional tone in the present. What occurred physically at that moment in the past is being duplicated in the present. This type can be very simple to heal using WHH or any power therapy, as the clients overall emotional tone in the present is the same as the trauma. During a therapy session, look for the long term, background feeling that the client has. The onset of symptoms occurs when the feeling first started, and can often lead to early childhood or even *in utero* trauma.

> **Example:** A man has been unable to work since a severe car accident caused him to hit his head. Using a TIR approach, described later in this manual, the client was put back into the situation in a car and asked to move through the motions of the accident while reliving the incident. This quickly ended his symptoms.

> **Example:** A woman's leg swelled, as if she had elephantiasis. Nothing organic could be found by her physician (of course, this doesn't mean that physicians can always find the organic cause, but in her case the physician was correct). The trauma was from an injury 30 years before on a beach, when she'd cracked her leg bone. Even though the leg bone was fine in the present, the client's body induced the same injury response in the present, just as if the injury had just occurred.

> **Example:** A woman had poor hearing due to tinnitus (ringing in the ears). Regression on the symptom lead directly to a number of *in utero* traumas involving very loud noises hurting the baby's delicate ears.

Illnesses maintained directly by trauma

In this class of problems, the body would like to heal the complaint, but trauma inhibits the normal repair mechanisms. Again, the current life circumstances are continuously triggering the trauma response. When we heal the underlying trauma, we find that often the symptoms immediately disappear, or immediately start to heal, because the trauma was in essence telling the person's body that it needed the symptom. When the trauma is removed, the body's normal repair mechanisms are then allowed to work, and recovery occurs.

> **Example:** A woman had months of constant bladder infection, causing pain with intercourse. Just asking her what her life at the moment reminded her of caused her to recall the first time she was raped. Healing it with EFT caused the infection to immediately start to drain and stop being painful. Normal healing of the infection immediately started. Note that although the pain was eliminated, the actual healing still took days while the body took care of the problem. Just because the pain is gone, doesn't mean the illness is instantly healed!

Example: An ambulance attendant injured her back while lifting a dead patient. A year later the pain still persisted. She regressed to the moment just before she picked up the patient, followed the feelings she had then backwards in time, and found an injury at the moment of falling from the fallopian tube into the uterus.

Example: A client had a long term back pain. She wasn't able to track it down to a particular moment. She got a massage and acupuncture treatment for her back, and noted the strong emotional and physical feelings that arose (a sensation of a bar across her back). She followed this later using WHH, found the origin, and healer her back.

Diseases or problems indirectly related to trauma

In this type of problem, the body gets a viral or bacterial infection to mimic the originating physical experience in the trauma. This can be a bit tricky to spot, because although the initial symptoms to the disease are the same as the original trauma sensations, the disease can quickly cause unrelated symptoms to occur. Thus, in this type of problem, the first symptom is the key to healing.

Example: The emotional trigger was feelings of loneliness and abandonment. The physical manifestation was viral and bacterial sore throats that would then become chest colds, with the sore throat portion quickly ending. The client wasn't aware that the emotion and the colds were connected, since the feelings were frequent and there was a lag in getting the illnesses. After doing WHH on the issue, we found it lead to vomiting painful stomach juices up the throat during the birthing experience. The client, later in life, was getting the viral sore throat because it gave the closest physical analog to that earlier painful vomit! Of course, once the illness took hold, other symptoms manifested, but that was the core problem.

Example: We've found that trauma often causes chiropractic problems. As you may know, the chiropractor often continues to adjust a client year after year because their vertebra continually move out of position. We've found that this can be caused by trauma basically telling the person's body that they need to keep the muscular stresses that move the vertebra. When the person's underlying trauma is healed, we've often seen that anywhere from seconds to a few days, the affected bones will permanently move back into their correct place, sometimes even with a very loud "click" that can worry the client!

Example: A client had parasite infections. It turns out that her body had low level feelings of loneliness, and the parasites caused her body to feel less alone.

Example: In severe systemic candida infections, a feeling of panic is generally present. The candida symptoms mimic the feelings of panic that the body experiences due to oxygen starvation during the birthing process.

Example: The clients' chemical pH was significantly too acidic. Regression to a time when the mother felt that her belly was ugly because it was distended with pregnancy caused the pH to return to normal. Finding the cause of this problem was by accident, not design.

Example: The client was underweight. The presenting problem was poor finances, and regression on the feelings using WHH lead to an *in utero* trauma where the placenta was partially ripped off of the womb wall. Although healing this didn't fix the clients money problems, the client suddenly found that he could gain weight, and that he no longer had any resistance to putting premium gas in his car.

Trauma causing decisions to be sick

In this scenario, the client has a traumatic experience that causes his body or heart to make a decision affecting his immune system. Often, serious symptoms are delayed a number of years from the originating trauma. This can be a tough issue to track down, as often the emotion and the originating situation are not related to the symptoms. Some practitioners report success using muscle testing on this problem, a good example of the technique found in the process and book called *New Decision Therapy* by Kandice Blaklee. Interestingly, the emotional component during the trauma experience is usually quite severe, even though it generally doesn't show up in the present in any obvious way. This can be used as a way to find the originating issue, by asking the client to recall any very difficult time in the years prior to the symptoms. An attraction to a specific piece of music can also be used to track the corresponding feelings to their origin.

> **Example:** In my own life, after a very painful divorce, I started to develop physical problems and diseases. Over the course of the next 8 years, I got sicker and sicker. Essentially, my immune system was not working correctly, yet no cause for immune impairment could be found. Just before I was to start a breathwork session, I was very attracted to John Denver's music. During the session, I played the music, and intense grief came up. The music gave me a feeling of what harmony with life could be like, especially with women. I suddenly became aware that during the divorce, I had made an unconscious decision to die (or more accurately, giving up wanting to live). I had felt that I would never be able to get what I wanted in life, and there was no point in living. I had been completely unaware of this. Once I felt the grief I was blocking (and actually unaware of in the present), I started healing physically very quickly.

Illnesses related to Buddha brain structures

I've come across a couple of cases where the client has physical symptoms because they have a Buddha brain structure, usually an inappropriate connection between two spots in the body, causing the organs to become dysfunctional. This also can generate feelings of pain or discomfort in the affected region, as if there were a rubber band pulling at the areas where the Buddha brain structure attaches. Healing the originating trauma dissolves the structure, and the affected organ or pain goes back to normal.

> **Example:** A client had adult acne. This tracked to problems in the liver, which in turn was due to a Buddha brain cable pulling at the liver area. Regression to this trauma eliminated the cause of the problem, and normal healing commenced.

Illnesses related to generational, 'energetic', or 'spiritual' problems

In this class of problems, the client's condition is due to a mechanism at what could be called the spiritual or energetic level. We'll be covering this more fully in the section on the transpersonal self. Although we believe the susceptibility for this type of problem is due to trauma, the mechanism causing the problem is totally unrelated to trauma. This type of problem is generally outside the scope of this manual, and is covered in the advanced training, but I'll give some examples. We suspect that this type of problem is actually very common. If you encounter suspect this is the cause, perhaps using a peak state ability, muscle testing, or by the process of elimination, I recommend trying energy therapies like EFT, TAT, or DPR.

> **Example:** A woman had a severe wheat allergy. The cause was a generational problem where an ancestor had eaten moldy wheat and gotten very sick. Using TAT solved the problem quickly. (Other approaches to generational healing are described elsewhere in the manual.)

> **Example:** A woman had chronic fatigue for over 10 years, and maybe a lot longer. She had what appeared to be a black plate covering her solar plexus, which was observed using the awareness of

a peak state of consciousness. The healer used DPR on her (covered later), causing her to let go of the plate, and her symptoms vanished.

Example: A man had in his leg a bullet injury from combat that wouldn't heal properly. The skin was grayish and had been for years. A healer went through the motions with his hand of removing something small from inside the man's leg. His comment was that the thing he removed was the intention of the bullet to harm the soldier, although he probably meant the intention of the man who fired the gun carried by the bullet. The man's leg immediately regained its color, and proceeded to heal normally.

General procedure guidelines for physical problems

Unfortunately, we don't have a fast and simple algorithm for physical problems. If you are interested in pursuing the area of physical healing, I would recommend an apprenticeship in a variety of techniques with someone who is experienced. Although a huge variety of physical techniques exist, from homeopathy to conventional medicine, in general I would recommend starting with a simple emotional healing technique like EFT and TAT. These processes are not physically invasive, reasonably fast, and amazingly enough will often fix the problem. Using WHH for physical problems is more difficult, especially when it isn't clear what the underlying trauma is.

Muscle testing (or dowsing, or applied kinesiology) can sometimes be very helpful in tracking down the any originating trauma or cause of the problem, but muscle testing has the severe problem of often giving incorrect or misleading results. If you wish to use this approach, a variety of methods exist, from dowsing to chiropractic, but I suggest taking the TAT training as they teach this approach in a simple manner. In general, I don't recommend this approach, and only try it as a last resort. Consider using a GSR meter to look for charged material if you suspect that your body consciousness has a counter commitment to healing.

Occasionally, the client is so ill or so young that conventional techniques can't be employed. Or it might be an animal that just tapping on makes no difference. Surrogate healing using EFT and TAT can occasionally be used with great success, or the advanced WHH technique using merging can be used. These methods are basically beyond the scope of this class, but I wanted you to know they existed.

Body consciousness resistance and muscle testing

One of the most puzzling aspects of healing to most healers are the times when nothing seems to work, or at best poorly, especially with physical problems. We've all been taught that "the body doesn't lie", and so assume that if there is physical illness or discomfort, the body is just showing that there is a problem from elsewhere that needs fixing but that it can't let go of it on it's own. This is often quite true, but more often than not, the body consciousness itself is not willing to heal or let go of the problem. The body consciousness is just that, a person, not a machine or helpless victim of our bad habits and tendencies. It thinks and learns by association of sensations together, and these associations don't necessarily result in wise actions or health. To make matters worse, the body can display amazing cunning while actively trying to sabotage, derail, or deceive anyone trying to fix it! In these cases, the body consciousness mistakenly believes that it needs the illness or problem in order to survive. This can happen for several reasons. The body has 'learned' through trauma to respond in certain ways, and will believe the associations it made even when it can no longer recall the reasons for it. Another is due to the shell telling the body how to survive, mostly inappropriately, such as when a shell piece causes the body to create allergic responses.

A good example of the body consciousness blocking healing is called 'psychological reversal' in energy therapies. This can happen in any sort of issue, but almost always occurs in cancer, addictions, and neuromuscular diseases. Another place this happens is in using the equivalent processes of dowsing, muscle testing, or applied kinesiology. These practitioners often believe that the body always tells the truth, or that in fact they are communicating directly with God or some other totally honest helpful power (in spite of tremendous evidence to the contrary). What is actually happening is that they are communicating with the body consciousness. Practitioners assume that their answers, if proved false, are being affected from a huge variety of outside variables. Although this can often occur, what may actually be happening is that if the body feels it needs to lie to protect itself, it will! This makes using these techniques quite difficult, as you never know when you're going to get honest answers, or get deception. We have had some amazing successes with the therapist using DPR (described later) on the client's resistance, but so far we don't know of any consistent method in normal consciousness to get the body to be willing to heal. I suggest trying the psychological reversal step from EFT - we've seen good results doing this.

Potential risks using power therapies on physical issues

We do NOT recommend working on life threatening situations such as heart conditions without the constant supervision of trained medical personnel.

At this time we have no actual evidence that using power therapies on physical issues can worsen an illness or create a new illness. However, note that when doing any of the power therapies, it is likely that the client will feel worse during the treatment than when they arrived as repressed painful material emerges. If the client has a history of heart problems then there might be a risk of inducing a life-threatening event during treatment. Secondly, note that power therapies can eliminate symptoms, such as pain from the client. This does NOT mean the physical issue was instantly healed also. Although the pain is now gone, the healing generally takes the same amount of time as any healing, such as a cut or bruise. Care must be taken to not damage the affected area. Warn your clients of this fact. Third, new physical symptoms can occur if the treatment removed a layer of trauma and started to uncover a deeper issue that didn't come fully to awareness during the treatment time, or that did but was not fully healed. Forth, there is a tiny bit of anecdotal stories that after treatment using EFT, symptoms later returned with more intensity, or new symptoms occurred. As these processes are state of the art and still being investigated, there is always the possibility that we don't know everything that can occur to everyone. However, if this problem really exists and isn't just an artifact of additional issues emerging into consciousness after the current issue is released, its occurrence must be very rare. Finally, it may be possible that doing anything that causes the client pain and discomfort, either through normal activity or by using a power therapy, might slow down healing especially in the case of cancer. (This last caution is based on muscle testing on only one cancer client.)

> **Example:** A man bruised or cracked a rib lifting a carpet. He was in constant pain, especially trying to lie down to sleep. EFT removed the pain completely. A few hours later, a friend gave him a bear hug, and the man screamed as the pain returned. As soon as the hug was released, the pain vanished again and didn't return. Obviously, the rib damage was being taken care of at the normal rate, but without any pain in normal situations.

> **Example:** The client came in with feelings of intense dislike for a man she had just met. This lead to a birth piece that the client was unsuccessful in healing during treatment, which included significant pain and nausea.

> **Example:** A client had a painful gut cancer. He wanted to remove his fear of dying, which we did using WHH on events around nearly dying in his childhood. The client then had the intuition that his cancer would heal more slowly or worsen if he continued using the WHH on painful events in his life, which muscle testing also indicated. Later, he went in for conventional surgery and the cancer was successfully removed.

Key Points:

- Watch out for potentially lethal heart conditions in your clients!

- WHH works well on the consequences to direct physical trauma.

- Physical problems are usually indirectly related to trauma, hence finding the correct trauma can be difficult.

- We recommend first using energy therapies rather than WHH on physical issues for its simplicity.

- Healing virtually any physical difficulty in minutes is possible but rarely accomplished.

- Muscle testing, dowsing, and applied kinesiology are potentially deceptive.

ON HEALING PAIN

One of the most common complaints that clients have is pain, especially chronic pain. Both WHH and EFT meridian style therapies can deal with it quite directly. However, pain is NOT a direct result of physical injury or distress, and this must be understood in order to treat it with consistent success. Although our cultural conditioning and personal experience generally says we experience pain as the direct result of bodily injury, there is actually an intermediate mechanism that causes the pain. This means that when this intermediate mechanism is activated, you can have pain without any physical damage, or contra wise have physical damage without pain. Thus, as pain is an indirect result of trauma, just healing an injury trauma won't necessarily heal the associated pain, and visa versa.

The biology of pain

What is this intermediate mechanism? Let's look at the underlying biology. As we've worked it out so far, after an injury first occurs, we experience pain as a result of two different internal biological systems going into separation and conflict at the injury site. Later, whenever the memory of the injury is triggered, this conflict reoccurs and pain is the result.

Thus, pain is NOT due to mechanical problems in the body, as the medical model suggests. One system is controlled by the body consciousness (the reptilian brain) and the other by the emotional consciousness (the mammalian brain) in our body. Thus, when we have an emotion ABOUT our body having pain, it's a way for our emotional brain to experience itself as separate from the body brain—it's viewing the body as separate from itself. With practice, our experience of pain becomes quite different. As one client reports, she'll have a momentary flash of pain due to an injury, which then vanishes as she lets the emotions about it go. Personally, I experience a body sensation that my heart settles down into my diaphragm as I release pain. (At this point in our work, we have found that the brain primarily responsible for pain is the Solar Plexus brain, which is often merged and indistinguishable from the body brain.)

Using standard EFT directly on the pain

Practitioners using EFT will have encountered how often they can 'tap' on pain or do a floor to ceiling eye roll and it will vanish or become greatly reduced - even though the underlying injury or damage is still present. Examples include the pain of a cracked rib, or the pain from arthritis and swollen joints, or the pain from pounding your finger with a hammer. I estimate up to a 50% success rate using the standard EFT process directly on the pain.

Gary Craig, the developer of EFT makes the following suggestion in how to treat pain using EFT: "To the astonishment of many, tapping on physical pains often reduces or eliminates the discomfort. This is sometimes true of long-standing, constant pain that has responded to no other treatment. (For an impressive list of results with this technique, please refer to the 7 part series on our web site starting with http://www.emofree.com/pain-i.htm). The standard procedure is to address the pain directly by starting with Setup phrases such as....

"Even though I have this headache..."

"Even though I have this stomach upset..."

"Even though I have this numbness in my knee..." etc.

and continuing through the EFT process.

When tapping directly on the pain becomes stalled or ineffective, it is then recommended that we start tapping on emotional issues behind the pain. I often ask the question, "If there was an emotional reason for this pain, what would it be?" This usually brings about success."

More comments on this topic by Gary Craig can be found at the EFT website at http://www.emofree.com/howdoyou.htm.

Using EFT directly on the intermediate pain mechanism

Here's how to tap on the actual pain mechanism itself. I have the client focus on the feelings they have ABOUT their body having pain, and do EFT on those feelings. This is the key piece. Then we continue in the normal manner, eliminating any additional emotions that arise as the "onion" of their problem peels away. To help people focus on the original feeling, I have them pretend that their body is a car that has some sort of ding or mechanical problem, and ask them how they feel about their car being broken. For example, a client with a bad back might feel angry his body doesn't work well anymore, or sad his body is wearing out, and so on. In some cases, if the client can't get in touch with the feeling, usually because they're so used to it they don't notice it anymore, I ask them what someone else might feel about the pain if they had it. We generally don't bother having them focus on the pain directly while doing EFT as this emotional approach is much more effective. We tell our workshop participants that one might get lucky if one focuses just on the pain, but that for many people the pain and the emotional cause are disconnected in their awareness. Hence, tapping while focused on pain only gives occasional or partial relief.

However, tapping on the feelings a client has ABOUT the pain is generally so successful that we always have people eliminate pain (not just reduce it) to start our EFT workshops. In our private practice, we continue working until the client is pain and stiffness free, even in cases involving medical conditions such as a damaged spine or arthritis. I estimate this approach eliminates pain completely in about 90% of the clients or workshop participants we see. Of course, the treatment needs to be repeated as new aspects come up, but if so we just repeat the same procedure.

Using Whole-Hearted Healing on pain

WHH or other power therapies that use regression such as such as TIR can also be used to treat pain. EFT eliminates the body's access to traumatic feelings at particular traumatic moments in the past, even though the client is generally not conscious of the actual traumatic memory in most cases. Thus, regression techniques can also be used, although it can sometimes be difficult to find the correct moment in time when the pain problem became locked in place. We tend to use them only if the meridian therapies don't work, as they're slower and more painful. Remember, regressing a client to the moment of the original injury and healing that doesn't necessarily eliminate the client's pain. (Although I think it's a smart thing to do for other reasons). However, regressing them to the moment they had feelings ABOUT their body having the pain and healing THAT generally does eliminate the pain.

EFT and WHH used together to regress these clients to the correct traumatic moments then using EFT to quickly eliminate the pain is another good option. This hybrid process is covered in depth later in the course.

Other mechanisms that can cause pain

If the above treatments were not successful, we've come across a few other types of problems that cause pain:

Buddha brain structures: Occasionally, when doing WHH, we might find that the client experiences pain almost as if there was a physical connection between two areas of the body, pulling the body out of place.

Healing the originating trauma dissolves the structure and eliminates the pain. Finding the originating trauma can be difficult, however.

Copying and soul stealing: Especially in chronic pain, ask the client if they feel the 'presence' of someone on the surface of their body where the pain is located. Especially if you find the pain can expand or contract like it's caused by something moving, suspect this cause. Also, if you heal an underlying trauma, and shortly the client's pain returns, suspect this mechanism also. Using EFT on the issue that the client is actually 'holding on to' the person is usually enough to cause them to release the copy or soul piece in that area. At release, the pain will vanish if there isn't also a trauma in that area. I've seen this problem in about a third of the cases of 'frozen shoulder' I've worked on.

> **Example:** An elderly woman had constant back pain. The problem did not respond to EFT or TAT. Using WHH to heal individual traumas would cause the pain to end, but only for the day or so, when it would return. Using an unusual state of consciousness, the practitioner caused the woman's solar plexus to relax, instantly eliminated the pain. The pain remained gone for several weeks until an upsetting family quarrel caused it to return. Repeating the treatment caused the same relief, followed some time later by a return of the symptoms.

Conflict between the biological brains: I've found that occasionally a trauma will occur that causes the brains to try and pull away from each other, as a child might try to run away from an angry playmate. Although one might say that this is what is happening between the heart and body that causes pain, it turns out the same problem with the mind brain can also cause pain.

> **Example:** One morning I couldn't get out of bed because my neck was in so much pain. It hurt so bad that I did the only thing I could do, which was hope it was from something in the past. Sure enough, it was from a birth memory where I was pushing at my mother's pelvis, and feeling my anger at that moment was enough to instantly eliminate my neck pain. It turns out that the mind brain had assumed that the body was angry at it during that trauma, and once it realized the body was actually angry at the mother, it released it's block that was holding the neck pain in place.

Suggested procedures for eliminating pain

Start with EFT or other meridian based therapy on the feeling the client has about the pain. Keep going until all the physical symptoms are gone, such as stiffness or soreness, even though you might think that such a thing was impossible. Note that often the client will actually tell you what the underlying cause is if you ask them, generally feelings that are due to situations in their current lives. If this doesn't work, switch to a combination of other techniques, perhaps with muscle testing to identify any relevant trauma.

Another procedure that I know works for pain in general is a procedure found in Tom Brown Jr.'s book *Awakening Spirits*. A friend of mine was in agony from dental work, and this completely eliminated it in just a few minutes, much to her surprise!

Key Points:

- Pain is not directly related to physical damage.

- The most common pain mechanism is the heart brain holding a feeling about the pain.

EXERCISE—PRACTICE WHH WITH A PARTNER

Choose new partners. Again, pretend that you're working with a real client. As before, remember to record the issue and rate the SUDS. You'll need to record the client's traumas, and if you don't finish in the time available, record the trauma image and the emotion and body sensation that you left your practice client at so that you can return to the trauma later. Then switch partners. You will each have at least 30 minutes to work (i.e. 1 hour total), or more as we expect some of you to need to work into the lunch break.

Make special note of any of the unusual things that you've found during the session so you can share your experience with your classmates.

You've now been exposed to most of the ins and outs of the basic WHH technique. This is the last practice session before we start to include material that isn't currently found on the website. Even though the process can still basically be unfamiliar, keep in the back of your mind that you are practicing this not only to increase your skill level, but to be able to comfortably and effectively work with and heal other people. This is true even if you aren't a therapist, as you'll find out that friends (and yourself, of course) will start to ask for help once you feel comfortable with the processes.

This is your chance to try stuff with an understanding partner that if you did it in a therapy office might make you look like you didn't know what you were doing! Like children learning, it is exploring not only what works but what doesn't that allows you to find out where the limits are and how far they can be stretched. Keep the communication between you and your partner going, what worked, what didn't, what they found intrusive, what was helpful. Often, what we think is helpful might not be, and visa versa. And this can change from client to client. That's why lots of practice and feedback can be so valuable in this training setting.

Practice Session Notes:

Practice Session Notes (continued):

A TRANSPERSONAL EXTENSION TO THE TRIUNE BRAIN MODEL: THE SELF, THE FALSE-SELF, AND THE SHELL

The self, the 'Center of Awareness' (CoA), and the unconscious

If the triune brain model is correct, why doesn't it match our everyday experience? True, we have thoughts, feelings, and body sensations, but doesn't the Western model of a single awareness with a conscious and unconscious fit our typical perception of ourselves better? Even if the triune model is true, isn't our seat of awareness behind our eyes in the neocortex? To answer these questions we need to include a transpersonal element to the triune brain model.

We start by looking at what many spiritual practices are trying to accomplish. For example, Buddhist vipassana meditation asks us to dis-identify with our thoughts, feelings, and body sensations. In other words, they want us to become aware that our everyday sense of self at bottom is independent of the three biological brains. This non-biological awareness, true self, or 'spirit' as it is sometimes called in religious literature, is the transpersonal element to the triune brain model. In spite of our cultural beliefs that our spirit is sort of outside of ourselves and generally inaccessible, what I'm referring to is totally familiar to us, as it's the core of our moment to moment perception of ourselves, the 'conscious mind' in Western terms.

An important self-test can illustrate this point. Take your forefinger and point to where the center of your awareness (CoA) or 'self' is. Some will find that it's behind the eyes, the culturally assumed norm. Others will find it in the chest, belly, or distributed in some region of the body (making it hard to pin down). Various spiritual practices, healing work, or intention can shift the location of your CoA. Your awareness can be expanded into all of the your three brains simultaneously, held outside of the three brains, shifted between them individually, or expanded into your surroundings. We suspect that having clients locate their CoA may be turn out to be a valuable diagnostic tool for healing or peak state work. It is probably correlated with the brain fusion and permeability of the shell. (Incidentally, it is by shifting our spirit into the heart that gives rise to the second method for experiencing OBE's in the present, as we perceive the heart's ability directly without it being filtered through the mind. One can also directly see one's internal chakras by shifting our CoA toward them, although it may require another internal state in combination to do it successfully.)

Then what is the phenomenon that our culture calls the 'unconscious'? Essentially, it's the actions of the biological brains when they're separate from our transpersonal 'conscious self'. As we've learned, the individual brains are self aware, driven by their own biological function and traumas. But this doesn't necessarily mean that 'you' are aware of what they're thinking or doing! One way to illustrate this point is to note that many people use the processes of 'focusing' or muscle testing to communicate with their body consciousness, a transpersonal self awareness (the conscious) communicating with a biological self awareness (the unconscious). As there are potentially ten separate self aware biological brains, the unconscious isn't necessarily a single simple hidden awareness. Although I've never checked this, I would suspect that if the CoA doesn't extend into the area of the brain in question with a tight fusion, that brain would become part of the so-called 'unconscious mind'. Incidental, we have found that the CoA can shift quite rapidly, and can occur without much awareness that it's happening, adding to the difficulty in staying 'consciously' aware.

Incidentally, the biological brains aren't necessarily aware of why they feel or act the way they do. It's as if the unconscious had an unconscious! For example, the body consciousness thought processes are composed of associations. If for some reason it's associated an action with survival, and forgotten why this is so, it will act in ways to carry out its association even if it's inappropriate. Thus, if it's associated an illness with some sort of stimulus, it will recreate the illness when it encounters the stimulus regardless of whether it's a good idea or not. Apparently, the body either has a difficult time or can't ignore these associations, especially if they are *in utero* associations that it's forgotten the origins of. In particular, the biological brains have great difficulty in ignoring the 'shell', described below.

To add to this mess, we suspect that the body consciousness, and probably all the brains, can get their awarenesses stuck in one moment of the past. The brain then act out what's happing in the past but in the present, with potentially disastrous results. We have observed that occasionally clients doing a peak state process won't get a peak state until their 'major issue' is healed. We suspect that a brain being trapped in the past may be the reason for this result.

The Self and the 'false self' or 'shell'

Those dis-identifying spiritual practices I just referred to are also trying to get us to change our consciousness, not just dis-identify with our organic being's brains. For example, Gangaji or D. E. Harding in *On having No Head* talk about 'dropping the false self', and experiencing boundaryless selfless awareness. What are they talking about, and how does it relate to our everyday experience? And even more to the point, why does everyone have a self in the first place that they have to work so hard to get rid of?

It turns out that normal human beings have what we at the Institute call a 'shell' that surrounds our bodies right at the skin level. This coating or layer is actually composed of many pieces in layers of different sizes that coat our body, and overlap, a bit like the skin of a snake. Each of these pieces is composed of a traumatically painful phrase and feeling. These layers overlap, and can be either hard or permeable to our consciousness. If the layers harden, our sense of self in that area is restricted to inside our bodies, and the skin feels like a solid, physical boundary. If the layers in any particular area become permeable or are pushed aside, we find our center of awareness now expands into the surrounding physical area. Our skin seems to have less substance, until in the limit of permeability it feels like we're just made of air, with no body or skin in that region at all. Interestingly, the energy that chakras put out, which feels like warm water flowing out of our bodies at the site of the chakra, will be bounced back if the shell (false self) boundary is rigidly in place, causing pain to the body. It feels a bit like we'd shot off a gun inside a barrel and the bullet were ricocheting around.

In general, stimulating trauma injury sites where a 'hole' has been formed from the damage cause us to harden or make impermeable these layers at the skin in the corresponding area - if an underlying damage area is stimulated (or relaxed) in our daily life, we tend to respond by hardening (or making permeable) the shell boundary in the affected and adjacent area. For example, these shell layers can be dropped in just part of the body, giving rise to such experiences as Harding's "headlessness". When this occurs, one experiences that part of the body as if it were composed of air, with no boundary, yet the region has a sensation of strength and wellness that we've only imagined we could feel. Less commonly, other people have reported that removing the shell can still leave a sense of having substance in their body, but they still feel they have no skin.

It is our constant awareness of these intrinsically painful shell layers that gives rise to our familiar sense of 'self' after birth, and that gives us the sensation of having a boundary at our skin. The other major effect of the shell is to make events feel 'personal'. (This sense things are personal is also caused by generational traumas, and often the shell is anchored into these generational traumas in specific locations inside the body.) In the spiritual literature, these layers form the so-called 'false self', although at this time I'm not aware of any spiritual tradition that realizes that the false self is a boundary layer at the skin. It is the dissolution of these defensive layers that many spiritual practices are trying to accomplish. At this point in my work, it seems likely that these shell layers are created out of whatever pure unbounded self aware 'spirit' part is composed of, but somehow in a solidified form. Certainly, the two phenomenon of the spirit and shell have a major ability to interact.

How is this 'shell' acquired? A major piece of the puzzle occurs during birth. In the womb, the 'spirit' (self or I) part of us that can be best described as pure unbounded awareness is fully merged with our body. Our sense of self is very different than it will become after birth. Stuff that happens to us doesn't feel 'personal' in the way that it will after we are born. We experience ourselves internally as very bright and large, and we're totally aware of ourselves and our environment, including the biological and emotional environment that is our mother's body. During birth, as we exit the birth canal, we pass through our mother's shell layer. As we do so, her layer coats us at skin level, and in the words of clients who can recall this, it's like getting coated with black tar. Typically at first the coating is permeable, and doesn't offer much resistance to our awareness past the skin. But at the first breath, in most people, the layer hardens and becomes impermeable, blocking our ability to feel the awareness of our surroundings as if it were in our own body. At this point, the false self is born, and causes us tremendous problems for the rest of our lives.

> **Example:** A woman described healing right after leaving the birth canal. She had already removed her shell (by a process described in *Peak States of Consciousness* Volume 2). During the regression, she felt her body covered with a sticky substance, onto which the judgments of everyone present would stick. All the judgments made that shell thicker and more painful. She felt her placental awareness sliding in between her body and that sticky shell, giving her a measure of protection. The sticky layer then faded off. She felt the judgments would have stayed if she'd still had her shell.

These shell pieces can cause a 'trauma stack' origin just by their existence. As I've mentioned elsewhere, the core of many traumas can lead us back to physical injury - but we've been puzzled by inconsistencies in this observation. Any given shell piece is painful, negative, and contains a phrase that guides our behavior, just like an ordinary trauma which also guides our behavior and is composed of a feeling, emotion, and phrase. For example, a shell piece (or trauma) might have the phrase that "loving people is dangerous", and so on. In psychological terms, they are one of the mechanisms that give rise to the phenomenon of dysfunctional 'unconscious core beliefs', or even physical problems like allergies. I want to emphasize that any given brain apparently cannot ignore the message that the adjacent shell pieces are giving it. Perhaps making the shell permeable, or moving the CoA reduces this effect, but we don't yet know.

How are shell pieces created? We're still investigating this. We suspect that people present at the baby's birth, not just the mother, can contribute to the shell layer. The shell creation may be related to how generational traumas are made. Oddly enough, even someone who dies without having a sequential biological connection to the next generation can pass 'generational trauma' on (i.e. their trauma occurred after the birth of the baby). We also suspect it doesn't have to come from just a father or mother, but can be from other people.

To emphasize, the shell at skin level makes events (especially traumatic events) in our lives feel 'personal', or about us. When doing WHH, we find it particularly hard to heal when however we felt during a trauma feels personal, perhaps by feeling that we did something bad or inadequate, and that it's really about who we are and our personal value. When the shell is permeable or removed, one finds that trauma is just trauma, and whatever pain or feeling, like shame or anger, is just shame or anger like anyone's, and not personal. This is a bit hard to put into words, but it's quite unmistakable when you experience it.

What I've been describing is in no written work that I know of. However, you can demonstrate the accuracy of this analysis for yourself in a variety of ways. One straightforward way is to simply sit down, look at your chest, and try to move your awareness into it to find whatever is inside. If you are committed to knowing the truth, and are willing to endure the pain, you can punch through each successive layer, becoming aware of what each one is composed of until you reach the sensation of 'space' inside your body. Once in, a slightly painful effort of will can open up the whole area of that set of layers, creating a sensation that your body in that region is made of air. However, the gap will close up again when you relax your attention. This process can also occur spontaneously, such as during experiences of extreme love. Incidentally, the eyes apparently can act as an opening in the false self, allowing 'us' to go outside the body, which I took advantage of when I mentioned punching through the boundary into the chest from the outside. Of course, once in you can continue the process from the inside and punch out, which oddly is much easier.

Another part of this shell issue involves the existence of 'holes'. To review, some spiritual emergencies, therapy techniques, or spiritual practices that activate traumatic memories or increase one's internal awareness can cause an experience of a terrible feeling of deficient emptiness, a sensation of lack which at a deeper level is coming from what can be seen as black bottomless holes in one's body. These holes occur at locations in our body where we have been injured, and a tremendous amount of our behavior is designed to block our awareness of them. It turns out that pieces of the shell are 'anchored' at these hole sites. We tend to use the shell as a way to block our awareness of the awful emptiness of the hole in those locations.

A much more interesting but painful approach to demonstrating this analysis is to heal the underlying holes that these layers defend you against. As the holes are healed, the layers become permeable. Unfortunately, adjacent holes have their defenses spread over any particular region, so a certain critical mass of healing is necessary along with a lack of stimulation to areas of adjacent trauma. (If you attempt this, I strongly recommend avoiding the solar plexus injury. Not only is it hard to heal, but removing trauma from this region unblocks one's ability to affect the world around us. This is a problem when we use it to play out delusional material.) This was the method I used to test my understanding, but I was still very surprised when it worked as predicted! Unlike the first method, I found that these regions that feel as if they're made of air now also feel intensely sacred.

Techniques to dissolve the shell are covered in the advanced Whole-Hearted Healing processes. This material is covered in this basic class to give a grounding for advanced work, and because it comes up occasionally using basic WHH or in doing generational healing.

Other shell-like phenomena

To our great surprise, we've found that it is possible to acquire what appears to be shell pieces or something similar from the conscious or unconscious intentions of other people. We call them 'negative thought forms' (NTF), although in the movies they would be often called 'curses'. For folks with the ability to 'see' them, they look like black forms ranging from blobs to spikes to plates attached to the outside of the body, sometimes penetrating inside. They can have severe effects to ones mental and physical health, such as amnesia, neuromuscular disease symptoms, exhaustion, an inability to heal in certain areas of the body, and so on. It also appears that the body becomes 'psychologically reversed' around letting them go, in energy psychology terms. This is outside the scope of this basic class. We mention this here because the DPR method in the next section can sometimes relieve or eliminate this problem in our clients. Rapid ways to eliminate these problems are covered in the Advanced Whole-Hearted Healing training.

Practical implications

The most important thing I want to emphasize is that at bottom EVERYONE wants to be well and healthy. A currently popular belief system is that folks choose their lifetime to suffer and experience a host of problems, but we've never seen any evidence for this belief. Instead, all we've seen is ignorance in how to fix the problems. In the extreme, we've all encountered the problem of clients, friends, or even ourselves resisting healing that is obviously needed. This is due to trauma associations, shell, and other phenomenon that are normally outside of our ability to resist or even to be conscious of. In the next section, we'll be covering one way to work with this problem of resistance in our clients using a process called DPR.

Key Points:

- The center of awareness (CoA) is the location of our 'spiritual' self, or consciousness.

- The shell gives us the feeling of having a boundary at the skin.

- Trauma feels personal because of the presence of the shell layer at the skin.

- The shell is acquired at birth, and is composed of generational trauma.

- The unconscious is actually the awareness and actions of the biological brains when they are not merged with the spiritual 'self'.

- Resistance to healing is imposed on a person through a variety of mechanisms, including trauma, the shell, and cords. It is NOT their deepest choice.

THE DISTANT PERSONALITY RELEASE TECHNIQUE (DPR)

(See Appendix C for an outline of the basic steps.)

We've introduced the existence of the self and the shell not only because it's a major source of human misery, but because you need to have tools to work with it. Some of the tools are beyond the 'normal consciousness' scope of the basic class, but some are not. In particular, we're now going to introduce you to a tool that can be done in normal consciousness that most people can master fairly easily.

What is it good for? Distant Personality Release, as we've called it, is much more powerful than we originally supposed. We've found that it can have dramatic effects in helping someone do WHH; can make a person who doesn't want to heal an issue suddenly become cooperative, as in the case of alcoholics; and is one of the best techniques I've ever seen for couple or other interpersonal conflict resolution.

This technique, which takes only minutes for virtually anyone to master, gives one the experience of changing the personality you sense in a person or client, and the resulting relationship between you in a very fast, dramatic and vivid way. It is very useful in conjunction with WHH while working with clients.

Background

We are used to thinking that people are islands that move around, connected only by touch, sight and sound. This model is completely incorrect. Although a variety of non-physical phenomena exist, the one we are the most familiar with is one that we commonly call a person's 'personality'. When we think of a person, we generally get a sense of who they are, and our reactions to them. We've been taught that these feelings about a person are based on our personal history. This turns out to be only partially true. In actuality, when we think of and feel a person's personality, we are doing a real time access of the state of our energetic connections between them and us. If we have no energetic connections between us, then we don't get a feeling of their 'personality'.

Visually, with training, these energetic connections between people appear very similar to hollow tubes or pipes that connect people together. They terminate in a sort of ball or diffuse area that keeps them from connecting directly into our bodies. Each or these tubes (or cords as they are referred to by people in the psychic healing field) continuously transmit a phrase and emotion between people. The message being sent is composed of the phrase and emotion that occurs during a trauma in our past that has been activated, and is held in the terminating 'ball' and connection. The phrase and emotion are the same ones we heal when we do WHH to heal the trauma. Thus, we send all kinds of messages, such as "I want you to die", or "You can't be trusted" or "I'm incompetent" between ourselves and others. Our trauma's are often running continuously, and cause us to connect with anyone who has a trauma that interacts with our own. In essence, we torment each other in this way because we share traumas that resonate with a feeling from our past that was similar. Eliminating the particular trauma that has been activated will eliminate the connection between the two people, but the underlying dynamic that activates this mechanism in the first place goes back to womb, single cell trauma and even precellular trauma.

Incidentally, sending and receiving brief messages through temporary cords are a normal process between people and between people and other living things like plants. Their correct use gives an experience of harmony and balance with the natural world. Unfortunately, this positive mechanism has run amok in our species. Between any two people, this cording mechanism can be nonexistent, painful, devastating, or even life threatening if it activates traumas that are harmful to ourselves. This is the basis of much personality conflict, difficulties that clients have in healing, and relationship troubles.

This energetic connection mechanism can slow or even stop a person's healing cold. Unfortunately, the therapists themselves are often the source of these energetic connections. When working with clients, a therapist can test for this phenomenon by throwing up a barrier around the client to break the links, both between themselves and between the client and other people in their lives. The results are instantaneous, and if this is the problem the client immediately feels very different. We teach this in the advanced course.

The best way to heal this is to eliminate in ourselves the trauma that drives these energetic messages, using WHH for example. This eliminates our side of the problem, and then if desired have the other person heal their side, or use advanced WHH to heal the other person directly.

Using DPR to heal another's personality issues

However, there is an alternative way to deal with it that dramatically illustrates the existence of what we have been describing, and doesn't require that we find the trauma, which may be hidden in the past. I call it Distant Personality Release (DPR). Interestingly, even with resistant clients (like myself), there is apparently no way to resist or block the process.

DPR does not directly heal people - what it does is eliminate the shell related traumatic messages sent through 'energetic' connections between people that can be so destructive. Its primary use is to speed up a client's healing. Secondly, it can be used to make a resistant or disturbed client or relationship become open to healing. Third, it's wonderful for couples' work for a variety of reasons. It can be used by a couple on each other and increases one's compassion for the partner dramatically. Fourth, it works on shell related problems causing pain and other issues like exhaustion. Although I developed it to use on clients, I've had clients who can also use it on themselves for these issues.

The personality shell

The part of us that we consider the 'I'—what is known in spiritual traditions as the eternal spirit of a person - is the level that we are working at when we deal with this phenomenon of the energetic connections. Around our body is a layer that with very little practice with DPR you will probably end up seeing. This layer gives us the sense of having a particular personality to ourselves, and acts as a barrier to the free expansion of our awareness through space. It also is intrinsically painful, but we are all so familiar with the pain of it we consider is normal.

DPR acts at this level of being. You may see people in your 'inner vision' as if they looked a bit like Christmas trees, with stuff hanging off them sort of on branches, and at the skin level is a layer made up of large overlapping pieces. Your use of DPR can make you cause the client to let go of the pieces that hang from them like chunks or balls, or the solid layer pieces at the skin level. DPR still works fine whether you can perceive this phenomenon or not.

Unexpected side effects

A note of CAUTION before you continue: I invented the method from scratch while investigating the phenomenon of unconditional love. Thus, it doesn't have a historical track record laying out any unusual problems that might occur. To investigate negative consequences, in one of my workshops I introduced this method and had the group muscle test the question "Is it safe for me to use?" 20% said it was unsafe for them. In the case of the only person I was able to investigate further, the reason was that she had a belief that you couldn't heal another person, and apparently a conflict inside her resulted. Bringing this to consciousness and tapping (using EFT) on her issue then gave the muscle test result that it was now safe for her to use. Interesting.

Another odd experience occurred when a therapist used it on me, around trauma in my diaphragm, and had the dramatic reaction that she felt she had been contaminated with evil. (A feeling of evil had been an issue I'd been working on earlier without her knowledge.) This was a shock to her and made her feel hysterical, but tapping using EFT on this feeling of contamination eliminated it instantly. To my great relief!

The final odd incident I have to report occurred when a nurse was using it on my father. Midway into it, she reported that she felt like her head turned into what felt vividly like wood. She was doing one of the steps incorrectly (#2), but withdrawing her attention from the process eliminated the feeling. We continued, and another interesting effect of this process occurred. I dramatically and immediately felt an effect on myself, quite to my surprise. After all, she was doing it to my father, not myself. My CoA expanded into space so rapidly that I nearly fell over, and stayed that way for a year. It appears that using DPR can actually eliminate generational problems from the succeeding generations!

I had one client report that after the remote healing by a therapist, related trauma spontaneously arose, but was easily handled by the client.

To summarize, this is an experimental technique and as such let the buyer beware, but the hundred or so people I've taught it to have had no other adverse reactions. My greatest concern is that the therapist might pick up the problem that they are removing from the client. However, EFT has so far been successful in fixing this side effect in the people who experienced it.

Distant Personality Release (DPR) outline

[Appendix C also has the steps to do DPR.]

Step 1:

Relax and focus on the person you want to heal. Get a sense of their presence. They do not have to be physically present for this to work. If you want to heal a particular personality issue that you feel about the person, focus on that, but in general in couples work just focus on whatever it is that bothers you about the person. You will get a sense of them, in exactly the same way you have all your life with other people. Nothing new here, or complicated. Examples would be the client's sadness, suicidal feelings, hatred of you, uncertainty, secretiveness, etc. Incidentally, if you can sense anything about the client, whether it is positive or negative, it is a problem for them. Especially in the case of a 'nice' personality, this can be difficult to believe, but this is because the personality level you're feeling is a shell or defense that the person has constructed around themselves due to trauma.

Step 2:

Love the client for having the problem. Rather than loving them in spite of the problem, which is what we normally do, feel it is the problem that is actually what makes them lovable. For example, if the person is a smoker, feel that it is their smoking, which makes them lovable. To emphasize this, I'm asking you to see them as lovable because they have the problem, and in fact they would be less lovable if they didn't have it! Use EFT or WHH or temporarily put aside any of your negative feelings about the characteristic or feeling you are trying to heal in them. This is a critical step for two reasons. If you do not, you cannot help the person let the problem go, and in fact you get into a power struggle with them as you try and force them to let something go. Secondly, this helps you eliminate the tendency in your own life to attract this particular problem in people to yourself. This is the step that people have the most difficulty with. If the process isn't working, this is the step that has gone wrong every time so far in my experience. (If you use EFT or another power therapy to get to peace about how you feel about their feeling, you still can feel their feeling even though you now feel perfectly calm, peaceful and lightness about it. This demonstrates that what you feel in another person isn't just a projection of your own personal material.)

Another way to get the correct feeling of loving someone for their problem is to recall someone who you loved no matter what, for example a small child you loved even if they were having a temper tantrum. Then get the loving feeling going, and bring the image of the child (for example) into the person you are working on. Feeling the love you had for the child superimposed on the current person seems to do the trick for some people.

> **Example:** A client comments: "Rather than fixing the trauma, I tell myself a little story that whatever comes up in the persons personality that irritates me, I tell myself that they're doing that in their desperate search to survive and get love. And in some level of their being, they feel they have to do it to survive and get love. And in spite of all the negative consequences of society, they are so determined to survive and get that love that they put up with all of that. It's like the whole world is against them, but they persevere. I've applied this to people who smoke—they get so many negative messages from others, with people ostracizing them, and part of them thinks it as well."

Step 3:

This next part is actually the part that eliminates the energetic connection. Now, admire this incredible being for their amazing ability to hang onto the problem no matter what. Realize how awesome they are for being able to do this no matter what's going on in their lives. Focus your admiration and love on them and how wonderful they are for being able to have held onto the problem so well. A step that can aid this is to imagine that the problem they have is like a cloud around them. (In some cases, it may feel like a shell layer to you.) And it's connected to them by some sort of cords, energy bands, rainbows, octopus tentacles, or whatever you sense at this point. Interestingly, this is what people actually report without prompting when you have them 'look' at the issue the person has. This sensing is useful to give you a feeling of the being who is actually under the cloud, but it isn't actually necessary to be able to actually perceive this level of phenomena. The process works anyway, regardless of your 'psychic' sensing ability. Incidentally, when working on yourself, you can direct love at the connections, causing the connections to break apart.

Step 4:

Keep your admiration going for a minute or so, or until you feel a change in them. Generally I just have students end after a minute, if nothing has changed. Now, pull yourself back into your room, look around, focus on your surroundings. Then focus on the client again. Amazingly, the client will feel different. If they don't, make sure step 2 is actually done correctly. Apparently, our admiration at this level is enough to cause the person to relax and let the problem go. This can feel quite dramatic depending on what you're working on. For example, one client felt hatred, and then the next layer down was confusion. It's this experience, which really strikes home the fact that you are actually working on someone else's psyche. Not only do they suddenly feel different, but often in ways that you would never anticipate. We have the belief that when we think about a person and feel their presence, it is a projection of our feelings about them, but this turns out to be untrue in general. We are actually experiencing them in real time. This will become obvious to you as the client changes while you watch and experience them.

Step 5:

They should now feel different to you. If they don't feel peaceful or vanish from your mental view, the next layer in the onion has surfaced and also needs to be healed. Repeat the process (steps 2 through 4) for this new feeling. Keep this going until all you can feel as the next layer is a sense of peace, or until they have completely vanished from your perception. In my own case, I found that the initial problem would return in time if we didn't continue the process down to the end point of peace, although I've had other clients who stayed changed even if we didn't eliminate all the layers. The reason they may just suddenly vanish from your perception is because they have suddenly (and temporarily) released their entire personality defense structure.

Example: One therapist has found an interesting variation on step 5. After the client was peaceful, she kept the admiration from step 4 going for 3 more minutes. Then, she suddenly felt a major new feeling arise in the client. After the client became peaceful, she again repeated Step 4 for another few minutes. This uncovered yet another major feeling. This also healed nicely.

Expanded DPR for Step 2:

While working on doing the DPR process, therapists found that sometimes jumping right into step 2 (Loving the person for having the issue, trait, etc.) was a bit daunting. So I developed this progressive process for getting into a place where I could do DPR. Following are the steps I go through for this "expanded" DPR.

Step 2A:

Close your eyes and get a sense for the person you're working on and for what "comes up" when you put your awareness on them. Let's say I'm working on my Mom and I get this sense that she's angry.

Step 2B:

State what you found in Step 1 in a way that fits what you sense.

"My Mom is angry"—No, not quite right

"My Mom is angry at me"—No, Still not quite right

"My Mom is an angry person."—Yes, that fits what I feel.

Now just sit with that statement until you can accept this is true. (Not saying that this is actually true about your Mom, but that it's a true statement of how you're experiencing her right now or that it's a possibility of how she is.)

This might be very easy: "My husband is forgetful" (when his forgetfulness is acknowledged by all and a running joke in the family) or difficult "My father is filled with vengeance and rage" (when you've never experienced you Father like that.)

What I noticed when doing this step and each subsequent step is that I was having an internal dialog about the issue.

1st voice: *"That's totally ridiculous, Dad has never been vengeful in his life and I've rarely seen him angry much less enraged."*

2nd voice: *"It's possible that it's totally suppressed."*

1st voice: *"But that's so far fetched."*

2nd voice: *"But it's possible don't you think?"*

3rd voice: *"Well it's what it felt like to me, come on 2, you have to admit that people can suppress all kinds of stuff."*

2nd voice*: "I suppose so, okay then—"My Father is filled with vengeance and rage" I can accept* that as the sense I get of him I right now.

This may be the various brains communicating, I can't tell for sure, but it's easiest for me to assume it is and go through each one and check in.

Buddha, you okay with this? Yes.

Mind, how about you? I'm with you.

Heart, what do you think? Are you out of your mind—this is totally nuts.

And then continue on to the Solar plexus and body. However, it also worked if I just listened to the dialog without identifying who was "talking". So, back to the process. When the internal dialog is quiet and "everybody" is in agreement with the statement you go to the next step.

Step 2C [Upping the ante]:

Take your statement of "What Is" and restate it with "It's okay that…" in front.

"It's okay that my Mom is an angry person."

"It's okay that my father is filled with vengeance and rage"

Often there will be an internal problem with that and the internal dialog goes on around and around until all the "participants" to this dialog can agree that: "It's okay that…whatever you're statement is."

I've found that there is usually at least one of the participants who is arguing on the pro side and they work to convince the hold out(s). The one time I tried this and got a chorus of "Absolutely not", "You're nuts", "Forget it", etc. I couldn't proceed. I was deep into a rather nasty little trauma and didn't have the fortitude to persist despite this unanimous rejection, although I suspect that the "I" that suggested this in the first place could have tried to convince all the rest. I'm not sure though since I didn't try it. When everyone is on board with this step go on to step 4.

Step 2D [Up the ante some more]:

Now take the statement and restate it this time putting "I accept that…" in front.

"I accept that my Mom is an angry person."

"I accept that my father is filled with vengeance and rage"

Again notice the dialog and continue till all agree with this. Then go on to step 5, which is just standard DPR.

STEP 2E [standard DPR]:

Now we're back to standard DPR so at this step you love the person because of the statement:

"I love you Mom because you are an angry person."

"I love you Dad because you are filled with vengeance and rage"

Again listen to the internal dialog and when it stops and all are in agreement be sure to actually stop and feel the love flowing from your heart until it's good and strong. Then on to the last step.

Step 3 [standard DPR continued]:

Now admire the person for what is expressed in the statement.

> *"I admire you Mom because you are an angry person."*

> *"I admire you Dad because you are filled with vengeance and rage"*

Note any dialog or notes of discord or disagreement. When all are in agreement again be sure to feel the loving admiration. Feel this also from the heart although to me it feels different than just the love—it feels like the heart is pulling the admiration from the other brains and funneling it all through the heart chakra and then out toward the person. So it's like supercharged love.

Then I stop, open my eyes then close them again to start back at the beginning. Feel if there is still a sense of the person you're working with, and whether he feels the same as before, different or totally calm peace and light.

What does the client feel?

When DPR is done with a client or other person you might have a relationship with, you may or may not observe behavioral changes in them. What you will observe is that they now 'feel' different to you, in ways that promote your sense of acceptance and peace. However, especially in couple relationships, there can be a dozen or more of these mechanisms present between the couples, and eliminating them all requires perseverance.

Interestingly, unless the client is directly observing the problem being released, they do not notice any changes as it occurs. When done simultaneously with regression techniques by the client, the effect of DPR becomes noticeable to the client. The phenomenon of temporarily dropping the entire personality structure is particularly fascinating. I'd had this happen while someone else was working on me while I was doing simultaneous regression, and I tracked my holding of the personality structure to trauma around oxygen starvation during the birth, perhaps at the first breath. This would tie in to other work that identified the time near the first breath as the moment the personality shell became rigid and impermeable to the self at skin level.

Ethical and other issues

Notice that this technique can be done to another person who is not present, with or without their permission. This brings up several issues in students: First, is it ethical to do this to someone else without their permission? For example, your spouse or employer is driving you crazy, you use this on them, and the problem goes away. Was that unethical? This is a question that you will have to answer for yourself - but from my perspective, what you eliminated in him using DPR was a defense that the person acquired, often very early in their lives, that he didn't consciously choose to have, didn't like what it did to him, but couldn't let it go on his own. Another issue might be if you don't finish a DPR chain of feeling because you've encountered resistance in yourself. Are you ethically bound to finish what you started? Again, that's an ethical issue that you have to decide for yourself, but I strongly feel that one must finish what was started.

Another interesting reaction to this process that occurs in students is the idea that one cannot heal another person. Apparently, this cultural belief can cause the student to refuse to learn the process or help others with it. Other processes that also involve healing others without their participation, such as advanced WHH, surrogate EFT or surrogate TAT, also get this reaction. If this has happened to you, please take the time to heal your resistance. As I write this, I can recall several people whose lives radically improved afterwards, and still thank me years after the intervention.

If you have any feedback from using this technique, please contact me at grant@peakstates.com.

Doing DPR on yourself:

Another way to use the DPR technique involves using it on yourself. Self DPR was developed by Preston Howard. He explains his innovation below:

"Instead of trying to love, then admire myself for how I was, I intended to and let myself FEEL loved for being just the way I was, then let myself FEEL admired for that.

Step 1

What I'm doing is focusing on a person I know. Then I'm imagining what it would feel like if that person was right this moment deeply loving me because I am what I am, etc. I'm not sure if it can be generalized or if it has to be associated with a particular person. I don't think it matters who the love is coming from. But I tried it on my friend a little, and I felt something "open up".

Step 2

I keep this flow up, and it does seem to start feeling like a flow. I found in one instance it didn't feel like love, but as I kept at it, it got clearer.

Step 3

Then, of course, I focus on that person admiring me for what I am, until I feel a release.

I kept trying it and it seriously feels like shell pieces being dissolved. I feel lighter and "thinner" if that makes any sense. The big problem was in remembering to do it, and then to be willing to do it on the particular issue."

DPR in Clinical Practice

Matt Fox who works in the field of addiction treatment offers the following insights from using the DPR technique in his clinical practice:

"I have had the opportunity to employ DPR in a clinical setting for almost four years with fairly consistent results. I believe that DPR can do for relationship counseling what the meridian therapies have done for trauma treatment. The technique is quick, easily taught to clients, and effective. I usually have the client use EFT on an image of the subject after DPR, as this seems to resolve the underlying trauma that allows the person to hook in. One interesting variation involves having the client work with feelings involved in the relationship, for example, "My mother is such a loving person because she makes me feel like a little kid," etc. Usually, this resolves the feeling in the client. For instance, one client related afterward, "I'm just really glad she's my mom." Occasionally, the client has the experience of having the subject of the DPR process relate to them in an entirely different (positive), manner. Other times, the behavior ceases and never returns. Sometimes the effect is just temporary, but when the behavior recurs, the client finds that it is no longer annoying. Occasionally the subject drops out of the client's life altogether.

As a substance abuse counselor who works with court mandated clients, I have often had clients who were resistant or hostile. I have found DPR to be effective in many of these situations. In fact, after using DPR in this fashion for about a year, it has become unusual for me to encounter resistant clients. I subscribe to the notion that most client resistance is a reaction to the attitude of the clinician, so I theorize that the practice of DPR may have eliminated areas of my energy field that the typical resistant client 'hooks into.' In addition, I find that my style of relating to the client has evolved into one of total acceptance of the client 'where he is', as opposed to where I think he should be. Finally, the resistant clients that I do encounter have features that may be typified as personality disorders. As I am thinking of it, it may be effective to try DPR on these clients' attitudes towards authority figures.

The following are case examples from my clinical experience.

> **Case 1:** This client was a forty five year old white male with history of marijuana dependency and IV cocaine abuse. Early in his active addiction, he had fathered a son through a casual sexual relationship. He had no contact with the child and was under the impression that the son had been adopted. He also had another son by a previous marriage. The relationship with the second son was strained. Hoping to improve this relationship, the client "put his son into the God Box." Not long afterwards, he was contacted by the mother of the first child, who stated that she had heard that the client was in recovery. Her stated intent was that the client should contact the child and establish a relationship with him. The son, now seventeen years old, had developed a drug dependency of his own and was in treatment. The client responded that he would initiate a relationship after their mutual substance abuse issues had been resolved. Contact by the mother quickly escalated to harassment, including daily e-mails and phone calls several times a week. The client approached the therapist, asking how to resolve the situation. The therapist lead the client through the Distant Personality Release process, (DPR), followed by a round of EFT. At the next session, the client reported that the harassment had ended the day after using DPR. Contact with the mother was reduced to a comfortable level, usually one e-mail per week. The client eventually contacted the son and initiated a relationship.

> **Case 2:** The subject was a twenty-five year old female coworker of the therapist. She was in a relationship with a divorced man who had a six year old son. The son resented the relationship and acted out against the subject by verbally abusing her, ("I hate you," etc.), kicking and hitting her. The therapist lead the subject through a session of DPR, followed by a round of EFT. The subject reported that the child's behavior changed dramatically overnight. She reported that they became friends and the child now stated that he loved her, and began to relate to her as a close friend.

Case 3: The subject was a twenty-nine year old white male, returning from a lapse in sobriety. The client was experiencing marital discord due to having phone contact with an ex-girlfriend, who was also the mother of his first son. The client would call to speak to his son and his spouse would become incensed at the idea of the ex-girl friend, resulting in an argument. After a session of DPR, the client reported that his spouse began to leave the room prior to the phone calls. The client states that all attempts to persuade his spouse to learn to accept the situation had failed, and that this new behavior was not the result of any communication on his part.

Case 4: The subject was a forty-year old male who complained that his spouse insisted that he drive and then criticized his driving incessantly. All attempts to resolve the situation failed. After a session of DPR, the behavior ceased. The subject reported that he pointed out the change of behavior, at which point the spouse resumed the criticism, having felt manipulated. However, over a period of time, the behavior stopped.

Case 5: The writer attempted an experiment with DPR involving a men's recovery group of four clients. Three of the four reported significant success. Later, one client reported that the behavior returned after he had informed his spouse of the intervention."

Key Points:

- DPR is particularly useful in helping a client do WHH, in eliminating resistance to healing, and in couple's therapy.

- Not completely loving the client for the problem is virtually always the step that causes DPR to fail.

- There is a small but possible risk of acquiring the client's personality issue.

EXERCISE—PRACTICE DPR

As I said in the write-up on DPR, the only problem I've ever seen with people not succeeding with DPR occurs when they haven't eliminated their own trauma response around what they feel in the client. And sometimes it can be a subtle remaining piece that's holding up the works. If the process isn't working, keep doing WHH (or EFT) until your response to what you feel in the client is to CPL. Then repeat the process until you feel a shift in the client. Be sure that you keep doing DPR on the client until they feel CPL also.

Notice - did you feel more compassion for the person you were working on after you finished? Can you see why it would be so useful for couples therapy? Do you think it might be possible to do DPR on your own personality issues? Is it better to do DPR on a person, or to have them heal the underlying traumatic issue?

Practice Session Notes:

Practice Session Notes (continued):

EXERCISE—PRACTICE WHH & DPR WITH A PARTNER

Again, choose new partners. Continue pretending that you are working with a real client by recording the issue and SUDS rating. If appropriate, try to use DPR while doing WHH with your partner. See how it might make a trauma where the client is struggling to be in body suddenly get easier, or how someone who is struggling to feel the issue suddenly gets unblocked. As the therapist, note that you can now 'love yourself' and do DPR on the client during the session. How might you deal with the difficulties of doing either of these things while also focusing on the client?

Switch client and therapist roles when you finish an issue. Figure at least 30 minutes per role, but feel free to continue well into the dinner break if you haven't finished in that amount of time.

Practice Session Notes:

Practice Session Notes (continued):

QUIZ #2

1.   Are there any exceptions to the principle of wanting to skip memories to get the earliest one?

2.   If the client sees an old photo image or made up memory when they regress, do you run it or try to get a real memory?

3.   What does feeling of heat often mean during a healing session?

4.   If you see some kind of dark looking structure in your body, what do you think it is and how do you fix it (2 different problems)?

5.   Does DPR fix the underlying trauma?

6.   After using DPR will the client's behavior change? Will yours?

7.   Does healing the underlying trauma eliminate energetic connections?

8.   What do you do if the trauma won't heal? List at least 4 things.

9.   What are the two types of unusual problems that won't heal with just the standard WHH technique (the 8 step version)?

10. What do you do if a past life memory comes up while healing?

11. Will your clients be grateful for the healing work you have done with them?

12. As a therapist, what are the most important things you need to do with a client before starting the healing process?

13.   Can your client or yourself get into trouble using WHH?

14.   What are the two different reasons during a healing session that a client may describe that they feel a lack or something missing, and what do you do about it?

15.   If a memory has pleasant feelings, is this a trauma that also needs to be healed?

16.   How many biological brains do you have?

17.   If you have a trauma that is similar to your client's, will he be unable to heal with WHH?

18.   If you are in the 'Beauty Way", do you still make energetic connections via cords? (After all, in that state past emotional trauma is no longer felt.)

19. Name a mechanism that causes people to get diseases.

20. What are typical reasons your client can get really cold during a basic WHH session?

21. If the fetus hears their mom or someone else say something during a physical trauma, can this be a problem? How about a very loud noise?

22. Can cords be located at different places in the body? Can you have more than one cord connected to a certain spot?

23. Can there be different phrases in a specific trauma?

24. Does the earliest image always have the exact feeling that the original problem that you started with have?

25. Each brain thinks in it's own 'language'. What is the hearts 'language'?

Day 3

OTHER EFFECTIVE EMOTIONAL HEALING TECHNIQUES

This section is a brief comparison among the emotional healing techniques that I've found to be effective. I'll be contrasting them with my 'Whole-Hearted Healing' technique where appropriate.

I generally recommend that any therapist learn EFT and TAT as an absolute minimum, before learning WHH. These are two of the fastest, most painless, and effective of all the therapies. A typical therapist finds they tend to use these 'energy psychology' approaches the majority of the time in their practice. Plus, learning them first generally causes the therapist to completely reevaluate the possibilities of healing, as they discover that most things can easily be eliminated using these (or other power therapy) techniques. In other words, their 'healing paradigm' changes, and I don't have to try and do that in the short time we work together in this training.

Given this advice, why learn WHH at all? Like any processes, different power therapies have their areas where they're the most effective. After using other therapies for a while, a therapist eventually discovers that there are some conditions that just don't respond or respond poorly to other therapies. Often WHH will work very well in those cases. Additionally, as we'll discuss later, we believe that the easiest and fastest of the therapies can sometimes be reversed, and in those cases it's good to know therapies like WHH that are intrinsically permanent. Finally, the regression process that WHH uses can often be included in the use of the other therapies, making them much more efficient and powerful than they ordinarily would be.

Standard therapy

My personal opinion, based on observation of therapists and my own training in a doctoral program in clinical and counseling psychology, is that therapy as practiced by the vast majority of psychiatrists and psychologists does not work and is ruinously expensive.

Why is this? From my perspective, the primary reason is the mistaken idea in this field that trauma is irrelevant to most psychological problems. Virtually no training or teaching time is spent on this topic, no currently taught models consider it relevant, and the single category in the diagnostic manual that even mentions it, 'Post Traumatic Stress Disorder', implies it is primarily limited to soldiers, war survivors, and a few unfortunate crime victims. As a student, I cannot recall the word even being used in any of my classes for the first two years!

My own work, on myself and hundreds of other people, leads me to say that trauma is the single key to the vast majority of problems people encounter. Fortunately, a number of groups outside the psychological profession have come to this conclusion, and pioneered a variety of techniques to heal. Unfortunately, since these techniques are not standard practice, licensed professionals in the USA risk loosing their licenses by using them, even though they are effective. Presently, many therapists who have chosen to use these sorts of techniques do so quietly, or get religious or alternative certification (for example, in hypnotherapy) to practice legally. Although these techniques are now slowly appearing in peer review journals, and can be considered 'standard practice' because of this, many therapists still worry about legal suits if they use them.

The other major reason standard psychotherapy does not work, in my opinion again, is the assumption that 'curing' someone of problems is not possible, and the best that can be hoped for is a reduction in symptoms (except in the case of a few types of phobias). This belief has lead to the bizarre situation that standard measures for psychological difficulties don't measure specific change on the problem the client comes in with. In fact therapists avoid any mention of the word cure in their work, which is a sad comment on the effectiveness of their tools.

Finally, the last major reason standard therapy is ineffective is that a significant percentage of the causes for people's difficulties are in phenomena that are considered unacceptable by the mainstream. Thus, birth trauma, womb trauma, past lives, spiritual emergencies, soul loss, etc, are considered to be impossible, and so a client with this sort of experience is treated as delusional, or else the real cause of a client's difficulties can never be allowed to be uncovered.

Alternative therapies are slowly moving into the mainstream, due to the dedication of many professionals who are committed to helping their patients. Until recently, these techniques were never published in the professional journals because they couldn't get past the 'peer review' stage of acceptable work. However, an exceptional article came out on Post Traumatic Stress Disorder in the June 1996 issue of *Family Therapy Networker* which describes the work done by Dr. Figley (the inventor of the term Post Traumatic Stress Disorder) to explore the effectiveness of four of the most popular alternative techniques. This, to my knowledge, is the first time these techniques have reached any of the mainstream professional journals. These core techniques were EMDR, TIR, VKD, and TFT, described below. Each of those approaches uses a completely different and unrelated mechanism to heal trauma. I've also added a couple of other effective approaches to the list below.

Finally, I'd like to say that in my experience, there are many alternative techniques that are also ineffective, although they often hide this by calling their outcome 'subtle'. Unfortunately, as the field is in such rapid flux, consumers have to evaluate providers in both the mainstream and alternative communities with some skepticism. But if you do choose to use a conventional therapist, be sure to choose one who knows some of the more common alternative therapies listed below.

CONVENTIONAL THERAPY	**ALTERNATIVE THERAPY**
1. Long term	1. Usually fast, 1-3 sessions
2. Expensive, paid friend	2. Usually cheap
3. No such thing as cure. Reduction in symptoms if fortunate.	3. Cure as in common usage
4. Model is wrong, little attention to trauma	4. Trauma origin of most problems
5. Poor tools - dreams, empathy, associations	5. Variety of tools and techniques: Applied kinesiology, GSR meters, EMDR, TAT, etc.
6. No unusual spiritual or fetal material considered acceptable	6. Unusual phenomena recognized and used.
7. Talk only - cant touch	7. Includes body awareness as well as bodywork approaches
8. Requires trained therapist	8. Often self help techniques with occasional assistance.
9. May resort to drugs with side effects	9. No drugs, no side effects
10. No legal confidentiality	10. Generally therapist does not need to know the clients story
11. Often cant recall origin of the problem	11. Some techniques don't require memory of trauma. Others get them quickly and easily

EMDR—Eye Movement Desensitization and Reprocessing

EMDR developed by Francine Shapiro is an effective technique that to conventional therapists gets results that are too fast to be believed. See *EMDR: The Breakthrough Therapy for Overcoming Anxiety, Stress, and Trauma*, 1997 (www.emdr.org). Shapiro had great difficulty getting it even partially accepted into the field of psychology, but it is catching on now, and it is probably the dominant alternative technique being used by the mainstream therapeutic community. No currently accepted model explains it, but at least it doesn't contradict any western cultural prejudices, and so is gaining acceptance on that basis. She restricts training to licensed mental health professionals, but it is so simple that individuals often do it for each other after experiencing it. It is also moving into the alternative culture under the label of Rapid Eye Movement therapy and similar names. The technique involves left-right visual, kinesthetic or auditory stimulation while the client focuses on the traumatic event. They might use a hand or other focus object like a light moving repetitively left and right while the client watches, or sound, tapping, or patty cake games with right left alteration - eye movements are not necessary. The traumatic event includes a picture, negative belief, emotions and body sensations. The complete EMDR treatment involves a three-pronged approach: (1) address the original incident, (2) address present day internal and environmental triggers that stimulate the maladaptive behavior and (3) install a desirable cognitive/bchavioral response imaginably to enhance future success.

Beyond typical emotional healing, this technique works well for Multiple Personality Disorder, learning disabilities, and mental content that does not apparently come from a trauma, as in dream imagery. It does not work for obsessive/compulsive disorder, schizophrenia, and depression. (As of 1996 - they may have improved the process since then.) It also may evoke some spiritual experiences after a healing experience is finished, as described by Laurel Parnell in "EMDR and Spiritual Unfoldment" in the Spring 1995 issue of the *Association for Transpersonal Psychology Newsletter*, but no effort is made to pursue this connection that I know of.

How does this compare to WHH? Fairly similarly, although I think in general my technique is faster. However, because they lack a transpersonal theoretical model, they don't understand how trauma is related to schizophrenia, depression, etc. I have a few cases where people using both techniques have had either better and more complete experiences with WHH, or they've healed something by themselves with WHH that EMDR was unable to help them with. This may be an artifact of the sample size, but I tend to think it's more because with WHH people realize internally what they're trying to accomplish. It just makes more sense, so they stick it out even though it can be painful.

At this time I don't know of anyone who does a synthesis of the WHH and EMDR approaches, although it's certainly possible to do.

We don't know if this technique is reversible or not.

TIR—Traumatic Incident Reduction

TIR is taught by Frank Gerbode M.D. through his Institute for Metapsychology (www.tir.org). It's a stripped down version of the methods used by the Scientology Church, without the cult trappings and involvement. Briefly, using a set formula they have clients relive trauma over and over again until healing occurs. This technique is very effective and fast, usually one or two hours per topic, and has the added benefit that they use GSR meters to verify completion in a clients work, since to avoid pain we can sometimes trick ourselves into thinking we've healed completely when we have not. Fortunately, the metering system can be used with any healing technique once it's learned. For rather difficult reading, see Gerbode's *Beyond Psychology*. For a more recent and easier to read description of the work, see *Traumatic Incident Reduction* by Gerald French and Chrys Harris. To help public acceptance, they do not mention the unusual spiritual and shamanic phenomena that can also result from healing trauma with their technique, but they do deal with it on a one on one client basis.

Oddly, this very effective technique has not had general acceptance, even though it works well, they've derived models of how traumas connect together, and it does not step on any cultural assumptions. Too, their metering technique, which has been around since the early 1900's and which I feel should be standard practice in every psychological training, is also ignored. I speculate that the association with Scientology has created a climate of fear in professionals who would normally embrace this technique.

I teach a combination of TIR and WHH for occasions when the client cannot feel the emotional content around a trauma, or to check for traumatic material that may have been missed due to WHH's focus on single moments in time. I highly recommend the metering system, especially used as a 'lie detector' to search out material we're hiding from ourselves. Interestingly, the one time I used WHH while being monitored by one of their teachers using a meter, I got a far deeper (and unusually quick) healing experience compared to TIR as measured by the absolute level of a characteristic called meter 'fall'.

It is not possible to reverse the healing effect of this technique.

VKD—Visual Kinesthetic Dissociation

This technique is based on the Neuro Linguistic Programming model. See Leslie Bandler's book *Solutions*. I've had no personal experience with it, but apparently it works well. It is somewhat the opposite of WHH in that the client is encouraged to dissociate from the trauma and remain out of the body to heal. In my work with clients, I've had a couple who may have been accidentally using the VKD approach, as they apparently felt no emotional or physical pain while healing, the experience of which is one of the major drawbacks to WHH (although the same result can occur if they're in an unusually good peak state of consciousness).

After reading about the technique from one of the inventors, I got the impression that the technique created a substitution of a pleasant feeling for a painful one. Obviously, this is theoretically the opposite to my approach, as I want to get completely rid of as much material as possible. However, for the average person suffering from a painful trauma, their criterion is an end to the current suffering, and for that it appears to work well.

We don't know if it is reversible or not.

TFT—Thought Field Therapy

This 'power therapy' is the original member of a subclass of therapies called 'energy' or 'meridian' therapies. (The terminology is still in flux in the field, but they can be classified in the same category as acupuncture.) Invented by Dr. Roger Callahan in the 1980's to treat phobias, this technique involves tapping acupressure points to heal emotional material (www.tftrx.com). I find it one of the most fascinating of all the current effective techniques. The client thinks about their problem, and taps various points on their body in a certain sequence, along with some eye motions and humming. The process usually takes 4 to 10 minutes, and is amazingly effective. Complex tapping patterns may be needed for some clients, but a standard pattern is effective for most difficulties. It is an ideal self-help process, and works on phobias, depression, addictive urges, anxiety, trauma, guilt, loss of a loved one, and other problems. (I recommend the simpler version called EFT available now, described below.)

I talked this over with Gerald French of the TIR Institute, and he suspects the technique eliminates the triggers to accessing traumatic material, based on what he saw during the training, rather than eliminating the trauma itself. This would make sense to me, as in my own work I discovered that even though the heart sorts and accesses traumatic material, it is the body that triggers the overall access process. Thus, for the vast majority of clients who simply want to stop suffering and get on with their current life, this treatment would be ideal. But for people like myself who want access to deeper levels of conscious awareness and understanding, this technique would not be as useful.

In addition, in some types of traumatic material, the process will not work without techniques to unblock the client's unconscious resistance, called "correcting for psychological reversal". This was also the therapy that noted and invented the term of the 'apex' problem that occurs with any of these power therapies. This refers to the common reaction of clients that after the process works, they immediately try to explain the lack of symptoms by referring to something they know, like "I just got distracted". The term is also used to refer to the common result that a short time after treatment, the client will often say that the healed material was never a problem, no matter how destructive it actually was. They just can no longer recall how painful it was, and often rapidly forget they ever had the issue in the first place.

TFT, like any of the energy therapies (EFT and BSFF for example) suffer from the effects that certain chemicals and foods can block or reverse the healing effect. In addition, it is possible to reverse the healing by using breath techniques that can happen by accident, as we determined in experiments we ran in 1999 and 2003.

EFT—Emotional Freedom Technique

Developed by Gary Craig, this is a later development of the Thought Field Therapy approach to make it simpler and faster. It uses a rote formula to do every type of problem encountered. At this time, I recommend EFT over TFT for those reasons. More information and a free manual on how to do it can be found at their website www.emofree.com. They also have a very good email discussion list.

EFT is an ideal therapy to mix with WHH. Although the inventors of these energy therapies don't realize it, their processes generally are eliminating trauma responses from the past - even though it appears that they're only dealing with the feelings that are present in the now. However, the power, speed, and effectiveness of EFT is greatly increased when it's added to the WHH regression process.

EFT suffers from the same potential problem as any of the energy therapies, i.e. that the healing is possible to reverse, via energy toxins or other methods like reverse breathing. However, this isn't particularly a problem in most cases, if the therapist takes good notes of what occurred so that the same core material can be 'tapped out' again.

BSFF—Be Set Free Fast

Another spin off of the TFT process, this energy therapy also uses tapping, but on only 3 meridian points. Its inventor is Larry Nims, a psychotherapist in California (www.besetfreefast.com). Although he personally uses muscle testing with the process, it's not an integral part of the technique. (As you know, I feel this can be a drawback when it gives results that are deceptively incorrect).

A major contribution to energy psychology was the development of what he calls instant BSFF. In this, you program yourself to run through the process instantly and automatically without any tapping by focusing on the issue and using a keyword to trigger the process. Time elapsed is usually in the 1 second range.

BSFF is also a reversible therapy.

TAT—The Tapas Acupressure Technique

Invented by Tapas Fleming (www.tat-intl.com), to treat allergies, she discovered that allergies were due to trauma, something transmitted through the generations. Thus her method actually has a much wider application in healing trauma in general. It typically involves using Applied Kinesiology (dowsing with the body) to ask the body certain types of questions, in combination with holding the head and touching certain acupressure points around the eyes while going through a four step (later increased to a seven step) process. Note that the muscle testing is not usually required, rote performance of all the steps seems to work in most cases. The technique typically takes 4 or so minutes. It is also ideal as a self help technique, as it doesn't require outside help once it's learned.

I've had her training, and saw unbelievable successes with it. For example, one involved a baby boy who had gone into allergic shock, and his mother did the treatment on herself as a surrogate for the baby, since he couldn't do the process. That baby boy was completely back to normal in around four minutes, with the heat and body swelling completely gone! A number of therapists I've met use the process with very high success rate, in the 80% - 90% range.

However, the technique has several drawbacks. First, approximately 30% of the general population can't communicate with their bodies to dowse, and so would require someone who could get answers for them, either by dowsing for them, or using Applied Kinesiology (AK) tests like the one involving pushing down on the arm. The next major problem has to do with the facilitator. After or sometimes even during the training certain therapist can't make the process work. This leads us to believe there is an element to the process that isn't explicitly defined, and so isn't passed on to the client unless the facilitator is unconsciously modeling it. We believe at this time that the client or facilitator needs to be in the 'continuously happy' state of consciousness (body heart fused) or better for it to be reliably effective. We've done some preliminary work to make it more reliable in normal consciousness, but that project needs someone to follow up on it. And like all the therapies, there is a small group of clients that it appears to never work on no matter what.

One of the drawbacks to WHH in physical issues is noticing the trigger sensation or emotion around a symptom. TAT bypasses that and uses the body complaint directly, for a very rapid, painless, and easy cure, often not even involving a conscious awareness of the originating trauma. One of TAT's major contributions is it's usefulness with generational trauma, one of the few techniques that addresses this problem. I would recommend this method to anyone who wanted another very successful and simple technique in their toolkit.

We don't yet know if it is reversible or not, but as of this writing we're testing for this.

WHH—Whole-Hearted Healing

Our own WHH can be classified as a power therapy that uses regression technique with the unique feature that it uses an understanding of the OBE experience and the nature of the triune brain to get it's results. Although faster than TIR and about the same speed as EMDR, it's not as easy to use or as fast and painless as the subcategory of power therapies called 'energy' or 'meridian' therapies such as TFT, EFT, and BSFF. It's advantage is that it often works when the other therapies do not, and can be used in conjunction with them. In particular, it does not have problems with 'psychological reversal' or 'energy toxins' which the energy therapies can have.

Basic WHH works only on trauma, and does not involve any other sorts of phenomena. However, many other types of problems, although not directly caused by trauma are started by trauma (for example, schizophrenia). Thus, WHH is more powerful than might be supposed once a practitioner knows what type of trauma to heal to eliminate problems that, although started by trauma, are not a direct trauma response.

Thus, certain kinds of problems require you to understand the generic cause before you can heal clients of them - schizophrenia being an example that we've solved. Much of the work of the Institute is finding what are the causes for certain kinds of conditions so we can apply WHH and other hybrid processes we've developed to them. Examples of these diseases that are still unsolved are addictions, neuromuscular diseases and obsessive-compulsive disorder (OCD).

The healing from WHH is not reversible.

Hendricks Body Centered Therapy

This was the first therapy that I found that quickly and repeatable healed people. Drs. Gay and Kathlyn Hendricks give an excellent description of their work in *At The Speed Of Life: A New Approach to Personal Change Through Body-Centered Therapy* (www.hendricks.com). In addition, they've also applied their techniques to relationship therapy, going beyond my more limited approach of just dealing with trauma in interpersonal situations. Their versatile approach has also been well adapted by Caroline Braddock to the treatment of sexual abuse. Essentially, they've developed techniques to provoke and heal issues by looking at clues in the body, and put a lot of attention on healing people's personas and interpersonal relationships.

I like their work, but rarely use it. At the time I got their training, I could not understand why it worked, so their principles were simple rote learning and I couldn't extend them into new situations. It's only been recently that I've come to realize the primary nature of the body, and the importance of joyfully supporting oneself in the present in order to face old material more easily, approaches that they stress in their process.

So, how does their work compare to WHH? One problem I've had with it is that it tends to require outside trained assistance to help spot stuff that we don't see in ourselves. On the plus side, they believe that any particular problem should take at most a few sessions, and that rapid healing is actually the norm. Beyond this, I suspect their clients can get at issues that are harder to become aware of with WHH, and also have considerably more encounters with a positive uplifting bodily experience they call 'essence'.

Breathwork

A number of related techniques all use hyperventilation in various ways to heal and access spiritual experiences. Holotropic Breathwork™ was developed by Stanislav Grof, MD as a substitute for his technique that used hallucinogenic substances (www.breathwork.com). It employs up to two hours of deep breathing and loud, often disturbing music. I like this technique, not only because it saved my life. Using the breathwork to break through resistances and open new areas of the psyche, then following through with WHH has been a very effective combination for me. It has five flaws in my view - the experience one has may or may not be what you've chosen to work on; they don't suggest scanning the past for symptoms that arise in a session; it tends to require someone else to handle music and assist, at least at first; they don't recognize the importance of the out-of-body experience, and so to avoid revisiting the traumas after the session, be sure to stay in body during it; and lastly, they do not recognize the triune nature of the brain, so that the significance of some experiences is lost. On the plus side, this technique is heavily oriented towards unusual spiritual and transpersonal experiences, which are expected and encouraged. It also encourages encounters with birth trauma, something most other approaches tend to minimize. Again, I highly recommend it, especially in combination with something like WHH. A variety of books have been written by Grof, such as *LSD Psychotherapy* or *The Adventure of Self Discovery*.

Radiance Breathwork was developed by Gay Hendricks, mentioned above. The hyperventilation is limited to under an hour, and only essentially soothing music is used. It tends to be gentler, making it more appropriate for typical therapy clients. Similar to holotropic, it suffers from the same drawbacks.

Rebirthing is the technique pioneered by Leonard Orr. A relaxed release breath characterizes this technique, and no music, but it suffers from a fundamental theoretical flaw in my view. They don't feel that painful, negative emotions are necessary to healing, and if by some chance they arise, they can be healed gently and easily, and so in my opinion they tend to block the chance to face and heal that sort of material. Of course, they would disagree with my assessment.

The Motherwave Awakening process by Kathryn Masters uses a wavelike internal body motion during the breath process (415-389-6122). She feels that this makes releasing traumatic material virtually pain free and gentle. This may be so, but I suspect that the process enhances fusion states, rather than healing trauma. Of course, if that is so then it's probably worthwhile for just that alone. Although it promises exactly what we all want, in terms of union with God, and advanced spiritual states, an end to money and relationship problems, and so on, I'm not drawn to it for some reason. Check it out for yourself if you're inclined to pay its steep price.

Primal Therapy

Arthur Janov is the most well known so called primal therapist, and the author of many books, most recently *Primal Therapy 20 Years On* (www.primaltherapy.com). He has refused to describe his techniques in his books, but the results he gets are very interesting. He too focuses on trauma, and is aware of the triune nature of the brain. However, his early work was flawed by a refusal to believe in the existence of birth and womb trauma. Eventually he came around under pressure from his clients, but he never gave up his refusal to accept any transpersonal phenomena, a serious flaw in my view. He also rejected Dr. Grof's approach and results, apparently a personality conflict on his part. I've never worked with his group, but Alice Miller in her book *Banished Knowledge* gave a very clear description of why she felt the group had serious problems, including disturbing cult sort of behaviors. Instead, she found a primal therapist, J. Konrad Stettbacher (*Making Sense of Suffering*) she felt was on the right track, and practiced his technique successfully on a variety of traumas. I personally find Stettbacher's technique difficult to follow or see how it would be effective, but apparently it is.

I recently had exposure to both Janov's Primal Therapy and the similar therapy used by members of the Primal Association. I was struck by two disturbing observations. First, the length and cost of the work, relying as it does on a trained facilitator. Much worse in my view was the lack of definite and finished cures - their model apparently predicts people will only get reduction in symptoms, rather than complete cures on any given issue. As you might imagine, I find this attitude unacceptable. However, on a personal level, I enjoyed the primal facilitators I met.

For more information on the Primal Association, they publish a journal called *Primal Renaissance: The Journal of Primal Psychology*, and can be reached at www.primalspirit.com.

Focusing

See Eugene Gendlin's *Focusing* (www.focusing.org) for more information. This technique was popular for a while, but by the time I got to my doctoral program in the early 1990's it had faded out of use and popularity. Unlike most of the other previous techniques, it does not heal old trauma for it's effectiveness. Instead, the current stuck material being held by the body consciousness is brought to awareness, and released. I suspect that it lost it's popularity because no academic model of the brain that could explain what was going on was available, and so became ignored as being some sort of fringe technique. Too, I suspect that because the originating traumas are not dealt with, the results are not as satisfying as one could wish over the long term.

I tried it, with surprisingly successful results. However, I think that it might be most useful in dealing with stuff in the present, and that other techniques need to be used for permanent healing. Focusing is basically what you do when you come up with the phrase in WHH, so studying Gendlin's book is very useful. Practicing it can make the WHH technique more effective. I don't know if any changes using this approach are permanent, but they may be as the body consciousness is the primary brain, and the other brains knowingly or unknowingly tend to act in reaction to it, so the technique probably has more of an impact than might be expected. It probably promotes fusion, which makes the healing process much easier and quicker. At a minimum it helps in releasing the body sensation part of past trauma, and in getting the 'phrase' portion of the WHH technique.

In the last few years, there have been improvements to the technique from one of Gendlin's students, Ms. Christel Kraft, by adding regression and trauma healing - essentially, they're converging to the WHH process.

Vibrational Healing Massage Therapy

Based on the prenatal and perinatal work of William Emerson, this technique was developed by Patricia Cramer, the founder of the World School of Massage in San Francisco (www.worldschoolsf.com). She works with newborn babies as well as adults to relive and heal birth and other bodily trauma, in very short amounts of time. This technique is one of the only ones that I know of that a newborn could use to heal those sorts of issues (not including massage and other bodywork to help the baby to realign skull bones, etc.)

It requires a trained facilitator, which is a drawback, but on the positive side a treatment sequence is not excessively long. And anything that addresses birth injuries is in my view one of the best values on the market. I can't say how completely healed these injuries become, but certainly enough so behavior is often radically changed for the better—even in newborns!

As an aside, William Emerson (www.emersonbirthrx.com) has probably the best catalog of in-utero developmental experiences and what the problems can be. They do trainings and have a website which I recommend you take a look at. Unfortunately, they haven't gotten around to writing a book yet.

Other valuable healing or related topics

Refer to Appendix H for other healing processes that we've come across and consider valuable. This includes books, websites, therapies, and other relevant material. A continuously updated list can be found on our website, www.PeakStates.com.

Key Points:

- EFT and TAT are probably the fastest, least painful and easiest of the power therapies to use. We recommend learning them first, even before WHH.

- TIR training is very valuable in conjunction with WHH, but we seldom use it by itself.

- The Focusing technique is relevant to getting the phrase in WHH.

- Body centered therapy can be useful with difficult traumas or certain clients.

- CPL is the endpoint for every therapy, not just WHH. (Although a lot of them don't know this.)

USING WHH WITH EFT

A brief review of how to use EFT

(See Appendix D for an outline of the standard EFT steps.)

The basic EFT process can be self taught from video and audio tapes, or from a free manual at Gary Craig's website www.emofree.com. Since the procedure is pretty unusual, I've found that showing Gary's introductory 10 minute video to clients or workshops very helpful. Once the basic EFT 'recipe' is learned, better results can be accomplished by using it in different ways, which are described in detail on his website. Different processes are being combined, such as the "Tell the Story Technique" below which is a combination of EFT and TIR. In the next section, we'll cover combining EFT with WHH. The processes are:

(1) The Tearless Trauma Technique (see www.emofree.com/trauma/tearless.htm).

Rather than go into and feel a trauma, guess its SUD rating and what the dominant feeling would be. Tap on that, sort of watching it as a distance as it were, rather than actually feeling the pain while you work.

(2) The Movie Technique (see www.emofree.com/tutorial/tutorcthree.htm). To avoid global generalizations of problems, have the client make up a movie story that's specific, and tap on that. It forces the client into describing specific events and experiences, rather than vague generalizations that don't work well with EFT.

(3) Borrowing Benefits (see www.emofree.com/tutorial/tutorkeleven.htm)

It involves tapping along while someone else is undergoing EFT. The audience chooses a personal issue, then the audience taps along with the client as though they were the client, using the exact same words and tapping on the exact same points at the same time. Interestingly, if you keep your own issue "in the background" while tapping for someone, you will likely resolve your issue EVEN THOUGH YOU ARE TAPPING FOR SOMEONE ELSE'S PROBLEM. You will, in effect, be creating your own parallels and "Borrowing Benefits" from someone else. Interestingly, there are no apparent tears or anxious moments in the audience as their issue leaves.

(4) Choices (see www.emofree.com/articles/choices.htm). Have the client pick situations that have been tapped on, and write down the positive choices that they would now choose to make. They're essentially affirmations but more specific and concrete.

(5) Tell the Story Technique. This is a combination of EFT with TIR. You can see live examples of it on the "6 Days at the VA" video (included in the EFT Course--see www.emofree.com/eftcourse.htm). Have the client narrate a SPECIFIC EVENT (about a trauma, grief, anger, etc.) and stop to tap whenever they get to emotionally intense parts of it. Each of the stopping points represents another aspect of the issue that, on occasion, will take you to even deeper issues. Conceptually, this is about as easy as it gets and it has a tendency to bring up important aspects that would otherwise take sophisticated detective work to locate.

There are a few guidelines to enhance the process and I list them below....

1. After describing the "Tell the Story Technique" to the client, ask them how they feel now about the mere thought of telling the story. Often you will get some substantial intensity at this stage and, if so, it is worthwhile to do a few global type rounds of EFT to take the edge off.

- "Even though I'm nervous about telling the story..."

- "Even though I'm afraid what might happen when I tell this story..."

- "Even though I don't like this whole thing..."

- "Even though just starting the story gives me the jitters..."

2. When the client feels comfortable about starting the story (perhaps an intensity level of 0-2), ask them to begin at a time when there is nothing to be concerned about. An example might be having lunch with a friend just before having a car accident. This tends to ease the client into the experience.

3. Instruct the client to STOP THE MOMENT THEY FEEL ANY INTENSITY WHATSOEVER. This is critical to the success of this procedure. Most clients are conditioned by conventional techniques to "be courageous" and to "feel the feelings" and to "be brave and gut through it." Thus, they are likely to go right by an important tapping point without telling you. The CLIENT NEEDS TO UNDERSTAND THAT IF THEY DON'T STOP, THEY HAVE MISSED A HEALING OPPORTUNITY. Hit this one hard. Emphasize it. Raise your voice a bit to punctuate it. Insist on it. Remind them that we are looking for minimal pain here and that they get no points for bravery.

4. Have the client repeat the story while doing EFT until they can tell it nonchalantly--like it was a shopping trip.

5. Then ask the client to close their eyes and VIVIDLY IMAGINE the whole event and ask them to TRY TO GET THEMSELVES UPSET by exaggerating the sights, sounds and feelings. Chances are they will get through it fine but, if they don't, then you will have uncovered an important aspect or underlying cause. Use EFT for whatever comes up until they cannot get upset about the issue by either imagining it or talking about it.

6. The ultimate test, of course, will be to physically visit the scene/person again and see if anything else arises. If there are any remnants left, they will show up during the "real deal."

This "Tell the Story Technique" has several benefits....

- It is easy to perform and, because the client talks a lot during the process, it often parallels what clients consider "real therapy." Thus the perception of EFT's "weirdness" is minimized.

- The "story" provides a built in procedure for finding aspects.

- It can be used either as a primary technique or as a way to test your results.

- It allows the issue to unfold as gently as possible.

- The client gives you solid information along the way that allows you to know how you are progressing.

When to use WHH, EFT, or a combination of the two

As I've said before, I recommend that EFT and other energy therapies be learned before learning WHH. They're generally simpler, faster, and less painful. I usually recommend that a therapist first use EFT (or equivalent energy therapy) and/or TAT with the client, given the tradeoffs described below. If they work quickly, you're done and can go home.

What are the potential drawbacks to using energy therapies?

- Energy therapies have the problem of energy toxins causing them not to work, or can reverse the healing when the client encounters the toxic substance

- The problem of psychological reversal with energy therapies can sometimes defeat any progress

- Some conditions just don't respond to energy therapies or respond poorly in spite of everything you do

- We've run tests that strongly suggest that that certain accidental actions by clients can undo the healing done by energy therapies, (i.e. that energy therapies are intrinsically reversible, see below)

- Energy therapies just won't work on some clients at all regardless of what's done to make them work.

The single biggest structural flaw in the current energy therapies is their lack of understanding that, in spite of appearances, past trauma is generally the cause of people's present issues. Since EFT and it's cousins seem to just magically take an issue away by just tapping on it without any memory of the past coming to the client's awareness, therapists don't realize the effect that the process is actually having on the client's past trauma. The second biggest flaw is their unawareness of peak states of consciousness, and the impact they have on the healing processes, such as understanding that the endpoint to healing is a feeling of CPL. All of these things WHH deals with as part of it's process. Additionally, WHH isn't affected by energy toxins, psychological reversal, is intrinsically irreversible, and will often quickly heal issues that energy therapies can't even begin to help, or are not very successful in helping. Yet, WHH is much slower, more painful, and harder to use than the energy therapies, and in some cases doesn't work nearly as well, for example when the client can't recall the earlier traumas.

However, another alternative exists. We've found that adding the WHH regression process to EFT usually drastically improves the already amazing speed of EFT, and allows issues to be healed that don't seem to let go quickly or at all with the standard EFT procedure. For example, EFT often see a client 'circling around' an issue, requiring many sessions of tapping over and over. Regression often cuts to the heart of it for efficient healing. So if you've already decided to use an energy therapy like EFT and there isn't much improvement, and TAT doesn't appear to help much either, I'd recommend trying a hybrid mix of WHH and EFT next. The combination has all of the benefits of both EFT and WHH with the only drawback that the healing might be accidentally reversed.

Incidentally, some clients aren't affected by meridian therapies, or affected only slightly. One man found that when he healed trauma in the first part of the birth process, where his baby self was stuck and couldn't get out, that EFT worked afterwards. I don't know if this is generally true, but it's worth pursuing if you have a client with this problem. I've had some luck with clients not responding well to EFT having better success after having some water to drink before the session.

How to do the EFT/WHH hybrid process

Applying WHH to EFT is quite simple. You do WHH just as you've always done, but instead of the painful, slow experience of the trauma where the client sits in the experience until it ends, you just use the tapping part of EFT to eliminate the pain. Referring to the basic WHH outline in Appendix B, replace step 6 with the EFT process. This speeds it up drastically and makes it MUCH more painless. Being in body is not as critical (step 5 of the basic WHH process), the EFT generally works even if the client isn't, but sometimes you need to get them in body for the EFT to be effective. Oddly enough, when I combine the techniques, I so far haven't had to do the psychological reversal steps that are sometimes required. This may just be an artifact of the small group I've tested it on, though.

For your convenience, I repeat the steps from Appendix B with the EFT change below:

- **Step 1.** Pick something that's bothering you in the present. Write it down, and note how badly it makes you feel.

- **Step 2.** Briefly focus on feeling in your body the feeling this situation brings up.

- **Step 3.** Recall incidents when you felt exactly like this (often the situations are quite different). Choose the earliest one that has a clear image. Jot down the memories you skipped over. Use the 'loving yourself' technique to help access memories if needed.

- **Step 4.** Place your hand on your chest to remind you to stay in your body in the past.

- **Step 5.** Move into your body in the image, and merge your past and present self. If this is difficult, try simultaneously: a) loving yourself, b) white light, c) relax diaphragm, throat, jaw, d) hyperventilate before or during, e) cranial hold (massage temples while holding occipital lobe), f) diaphragm massage, g) position at time of trauma, h) rhythmic wavelike motion. See text for details.

- **Step 6.** Use the EFT process to eliminate all the emotional and physical components of the trauma.

- **Step 7.** If an earlier memory image appeared, move to that moment and repeat step 6. Continue to earlier and earlier memories until no more arise. Use the 'loving yourself' technique to access earlier memories. The earliest memory always involves damage to the body, and there may be several damage memories in a series.

- **Step 8.** Check your work. The out of body image should be gone, with only an in-body image. If you flash to the memory, there should be no twinge of pain. Memories that you skipped over should no longer have any feeling to them. In womb, body should feel large and bright. Return to the present. You should no longer feel anything at all about the current situation except calm, peace, and lightness. If some new feeling about the situation has arisen, repeat the entire process over and over until nothing is left.

With this process as a basic outline, there are several variations that you might want to try:

- Some of our students have suggested that it might work to remove most of the charge from a trauma using tapping, but finish off the last of it using WHH, in order to make the healing irreversible. Of course, timing it so that there is some pain left over is not possible, but the idea certainly helps the client's suffering! In fact, we now suspect that shell related material causes emotionally painful events to be locked in place even if no injury is present (post birth, of course. However, this is still under investigation.

- Another suggestion is to use the EFT or TAT process itself to unblock resistance to locating the trauma.

- Again, one of the biggest problems in the field of energy therapies, not just EFT, is not knowing that the endpoint to healing a trauma is a feeling of CPL. I've often seen other therapists stop too soon when the client started to feel a positive emotion. As I've stated, even positive emotions are a problem when they are stuck due to trauma, since they then guide our behavior in the present inappropriately. (An extreme example of this would be someone stuck in the pleasant feeling 'manic' phase of manic depression. Both extremes cause dysfunctional behavior.)

- If you decide to use an energy therapy, note down the sequence of trauma. That way, if it becomes reversed, you can jump directly to the origin and re-tap on that, saving time and stress on the client.

Surrogate EFT

It is possible to have the therapist tap on themselves while their attention is focused on the client, becoming the client as it were, and have the client's symptoms go away. Called surrogate tapping, it generally isn't as reliable as directly tapping on the client. However, a number of therapists tap on themselves while their client is also tapping on themselves to try and boost the effectiveness of the therapy. I wouldn't doubt that a similar procedure might act to increase the effectiveness of WHH or the WHH/EFT hybrid process. However, I suspect that there is risk that the therapist might occasionally pick up the clients issue (copying), and so I tend to not emphasize it in this class. Clearly, there are times when it is very useful, such as with babies, animals, incapacitated people, and so on. Also, ethical issues need to be addressed around using this technique on people who can't or won't give permission. Advanced WHH is designed to do surrogate healing, and this topic is covered in great depth in that class.

Reversing (undoing) the healing of EFT

(Refer to Appendix E for a write up on the experiment we ran to try and reverse EFT.)

We ran an experiment several years ago to see if we could reverse the healing effects of EFT on trauma that participants had just tapped into CPL. One of the participants discovered that breathing unnaturally while focused on the trauma would often reverse the healing. The steps that we came up with later to reverse EFT more consistently are as follows. Not every step is required to undo every trauma, issue, or condition.

- **Step 1:** Focus on the problem feeling, just as if doing normal EFT

- **Step 2:** Tense the diaphragm and throat. One way this can be done is to breath in a way that is the opposite of normal breathing, i.e., suck up the diaphragm on an in breath while tensing the throat.

- **Step 3:** Initiate a sort of shuddery sensation, as if one were cold, with the kinesthetic feeling of pulling into oneself, as if pulling a blanket tight over one's body. This last step is not necessary in many cases.

  > **Example:** A client inadvertently reversed healing we'd done with EFT. She had an issue involving the feeling of dying. After successful treatment, involving a womb trauma, her experience of everyday life radically improved. Eight days later, after a kayaking trip, her improved condition reversed itself. What happened was as follows: she was kayaking, and it looked like they would all be killed in bad weather on the ocean. She was feeling that she might die (Step 1). She was frantically paddling, straining and breathing hard as she fought the waves (Step 2). And she was cold after hours in the water (step 3). The reversal of healing was dramatically noted after that by the client.

We have the following recommendations when using energy therapies:

1. Continue to use EFT and it's cousins mostly as we always have, because under most circumstances they are still fast, simple, and effective therapies. Their use is an incredible boon to suffering clients, and is radically changing the expectations of clients, therapists, and performance coaches worldwide.

2. Take good notes during a session so that for difficult cases the client can quickly get back to the core issue of the presenting problem if the EFT becomes undone.

3. For severe trauma which would be difficult for the client to face or access by themselves, such as birth or womb injury, I would recommend using a non-meridian based power therapy, such as WHH (Whole-Hearted Healing) or TIR (Traumatic Incident Reduction).

4. I hope other researchers involved in developing energy techniques look into isolating more accurately how to undo EFT (and related meridian therapies), with an eye towards finding a fix for this problem. This research could be valuable work for other reasons, as it might lead to a simple solution to the 'energy toxin' problem.

Recently, a therapist encountered the reversal problem in a client. As soon as the EFT was finished, the client reversed it. The therapist noticed that the client was doing the reverse breathing noted above as a normal breathing pattern after tapping, so tried actually doing tapping while the client was deliberately reverse breathing and focusing on the trauma. The tapping then no longer reversed. I don't know if this is generally applicable, but it's the first thing we've found to help this problem.

Key Points:

• Using EFT with regression as in WHH can drastically improve the EFT results.

• CPL is the endpoint of healing trauma for energy therapies as well as WHH.

• Evidence strongly suggests that energy therapies are intrinsically reversible from several causes, and precautions should be taken to compensate for this problem.

USING WHH WITH TIR

Generally, I don't find TIR (viewing) nearly as useful or popular as the energy therapies. However, if you have the time and resources, I do recommend taking the training, because it's focused on making therapists be able to really be present and helpful to the clients (particularly by not analyzing or speaking to the clients while they work!) The TIR process also trains therapists in using the GSR (Galvanic Skin Response) metering system, which gives valuable feedback to therapists so that they can get visual feedback on their intuitive sense of how a client is doing. The metering system has other uses, as I've already mentioned earlier. The other valuable feature has to do with their training on how traumas interact and connect, and it's worth the training just for that. But be aware that you probably will rarely use the process in your practice.

Yet, the principle of TIR is very useful in a WHH session for two reasons. I've already mentioned that using the repetitive nature of TIR while doing a WHH session is particularly useful for clients that can't feel the emotional or physical aspects of the trauma they're trying to heal. The second reason has to do with the difference between the two approaches, and how the TIR approach when added to the WHH approach is more beneficial (in some kinds of traumas) than either is alone. TIR emphasizes healing all the different traumas that can occur during an interval of time, while WHH emphasizes just a particular moment in time (the image). Combining the two approaches by doing in-body WHH while going through the time interval can be particularly important in totally healing an incident.

Let's look at an example. The client comes in with the problem that whenever they hear a police siren, they break into tears. Doing WHH on them quickly brings them back to the moment when they were a hostage in a bank holdup, and it looked like the robber would not only kill the client, but the other helpless patrons who had been in the bank at the time. Healing the moment with the relevant image with WHH eliminates the feeling, and normally one just continues to find earlier trauma in the trauma stack, until the whole thing is permanently removed. Yet, the hostage incident takes quite a bit of time, not just one moment, and there is a lot of trauma around it that clearly would show up in the client's life in other ways, not just in the presenting problem. Thus, after conferring with the client, it would probably be in their best interests to go back to the holdup incident and have them stay in body while they slowly go through all of the trauma moments that occurred.

Let's get specific. What one finds is that as a new painful moment in the sequence occurs, they feel new pain, and probably pop out-of-body. You just stop, move back to the OBE, and stay there till it's healed, then move forward. It's very much like having control of a video - you can go in slow motion through time, freeze frame, or go quickly through time where nothing much is happening. When doing this, I try to do as complete a job as possible, then start the whole process over again, running the trauma from the beginning to the end to see if there is anything that I missed or skipped over. And I keep doing it till the trauma incident is completely sensation and emotion free.

> **Example:** Adam Waisel describes using TIR with WHH: "I'm working on a generational trauma having to do with a pogrom in the Ukraine (1918 as far as I can place it). In it I arrive at my hometown to find it devastated, many people massacred brutally, including my own family. It was one of the most difficult traumas I've done, and I'm not sure I've finished it. But the point I want to make, regarding "using other techniques with WHH", is this: when I first got to the trauma, I tried to WHH it, but couldn't, it was too emotionally loaded. So for the first few days I used the T.I.R. technique of recapitulating the events chronologically, and only after I felt it was mostly healed, with the brunt of the emotions spent, I used WHH to finish the healing. I have used this technique also with my patients in very difficult traumas, to good effect."

Another way that this type of problem can show up is as follows: As you work with healing, you might be surprised to find yourself back at a trauma that you were sure you healed. This might be the phenomenon of what I call staccato or multiple trauma. This occurs when a trauma lasts long enough and changes enough so that you actually have several traumatic memories packed together. You will store multiple traumatic images, although somewhat similar in appearance, as you go out of your body several times during the incident. Birth is a drastic example of just such a phenomenon. Fortunately, you heal the new (albeit perhaps similar) image in just the same way. If you suspect that this is happening, I'd suggest doing the process outlined above to see if anything else gets flushed up.

USING WHH WITH TAT

The two processes can be used together, but I recommend learning TAT for another reason. We believe that TAT is particularly useful (if you have the ability to successfully use it) for problems of a generational nature. Although WHH can heal those also, it is a lot harder to get the client to regress to that level. Thus, using TAT either first, or in combination with WHH is fast and efficient. Additionally, we suspect that unlike EFT it may sometimes be reversible and sometimes cannot be reversed. We're running tests on this now.

Like EFT, TAT is also a therapy that can be used on another person (or baby or animal) without having the client participate. Called surrogate TAT, it works fairly similarly to surrogate EFT. The same warnings and ethical issues apply.

Zivorad Slavinski has a variation to TAT that doesn't use muscle testing. It can be found in his book PEAT.

USING WHH WITH OTHER THERAPIES

The effectiveness of the WHH process can be greatly increased by using other therapies with it. I've already mentioned several in this manual, for example Hendrick's body-centered therapy which I highly recommend. As most of you bring a wealth of knowledge on other healing techniques, I suggest you try combining what you already know with the core of WHH, the understanding of the significance of the OBE image.

Several of our students have asked about using other technologies with WHH, such as binaural beat processes (Monroe's 'Hemisync', Centerpointe's 'Holosync', brain frequency noise software, etc.). As of this writing, we haven't experimented with these fascinating approaches and WHH, but we hope to some time in the future. If you would like to pursue this, please contact us!

I also recommend that you get more experience and training on techniques that work with pre- and perinatal trauma, because these kinds of trauma come up so often in the WHH process. In general, your clients will find it easier to access these traumas if you've had more exposure to them yourself. For example, William Emerson in California does excellent trainings. Various breathwork techniques that work with these traumas are also very useful, such as Hendricks, Grof's, and so on.

In particular, our students have found several other techniques that worked well together with WHH: Gendlin's 'Focusing'; and Levine's 'Somatic Experiencing'.

Focusing

As you've read, the focusing technique is ideal for getting the phrase the mind stores during trauma. Dr. Adam Waisel came up with this variation to help him and his clients find relevant trauma images to heal. Dr. Waisel offers these steps:

"I only use the Focusing to 'find me a memory', sort of like a bloodhound on the trail. I let it 'sniff' my intention - feeling for the 'felt sense' of what I'm looking for - then after I get some 'felt sense' and it's 'handle', I ask for an image or picture of the memory. Then, the minute I get an image, I let go of the Focusing and revert to WHH.

Step 1: I start by Focusing on an issue (problem in the present I want to find the core trauma of, past memory I can't access, recurrent tendency I have that disturbs me, etc.) and feeling for the 'felt sense' of it. I get the 'felt sense' and the 'handle', and ask for a relevant image.

Step 2: When I have an image of myself (as an infant or fetus/baby) I let go of the Focusing and begin WHH with the image+ 'felt sense' as body sensation + 'handle' as emotion + phrase.

At first I was afraid to lose the image if I don't go for it immediately, but after some trials I saw that even if I lose it I can always come back to it easily, either by bringing it up as I remember it from the Focusing, or by going the whole way from the beginning with focusing on the same issue again (depends how much time has elapsed since I got the image in the first place). I have a problem with images, as I told you, as I don't usually see them clearly, and hence have to work with a very fuzzy, indistinct image. Another problem is that I don't always get an emotion with the image, and have to guess at it. Sometimes it then brings the correct emotion into focus, sometimes not."

Somatic Experiencing

As I've said, I found over time that expressing emotions during a WHH session only slowed the process down. However, how about body motions? During a WHH session, some people find their body wants to spontaneously move, and allowing this motion eases and speeds the process. Peter Levine's Somatic Experiencing therapy uses this tendency to heal. Two of my advanced colleagues report that they got much better results with the WHH when they included the Somatic Experiencing to it.

Rev. Richard Hunt offers this observation:

"I've been reading the website of Peter Levine on healing trauma and the necessity of completing somatic movements to release the gut brain trauma around the event. It explained what was happening to me spontaneously when processing things with WHH. Very often I would spontaneously go into shuddering, spastic movements and quick short breathing along with a tight diaphragm. I now realize that I was releasing the somatic component of the trauma.

I was reflecting on this and realized that when I was being healed by a local Qi Gong master, she would deliberately provoke such as somatic response and this was regarded as essential to the healing process. It worked, but I also realize that she only has a part of the picture because she did not account for the heart and head brains.

I'd consider incorporating Levine's work into ours. He points out that severe trauma should never be approached directly without re-traumatizing the client. His somatic approach is indirect and less threatening to the client's stability. Perhaps we need to approach a severe trauma in stages -do the gut brain physical injury thing of Levine first, and then tackle the more explosive heart and head brain aspects of the trauma. Perhaps Levine's approach incorporated into our protocol would increase the percentage rate of cures we would be able to effect."

Maarten Willemsen states it even more strongly, in a letter about how the body thinks and how it communicates with the heart and the mind:

Pain and Pleasure:

When I look at my own experiences and recapitulate what I know from various books, I think that the body communicates with/tries to control the other brains primarily through pain and pleasure. The cybernetician Stafford Beer created a term 'algedonic control' from algos—pain and hedos—pleasure. Pain and pleasure determine to a great extent how resources are allocated in an organization and an organism.

The fight/flight/freeze response:

Peter A. Levine in his book *Awakening the Tiger—Healing Trauma* writes that trauma on the body level comes with contraction, arousal, freezing/immobility (shock response) and dissociation. Dissociation is the out-of-body experience, created by the heart. So the body would communicate through contraction—expansion, arousal—relaxation (i.e. sympathetic—parasympathetic control), fragmenting (OBE)—centering (IBE), freezing/immobility—releasing/shivering/movement (fight or flight). Relaxation and expansion are called shifting in Focusing.

Levine also states that post-traumatic stress is caused because the aroused energy in the body is not released through movement (fight, flight or shivering/crying), but frozen in the shock response. To contain these huge energies the body creates the symptoms of PTSD. The blocked energies start to contaminate the emotions (heart) and also the thinking apparatus (head). He recommends to release these energies through 'somatic experiencing'. That's how he named his method. It's done through focusing on one's body sensations and the involuntary body movements that are connected to a traumatic incident or an issue (when the incident is not accessible in the beginning). The bodily intentions that were blocked by the shock response or were otherwise frustrated have to be finished by executing them.

An important step in his method is to differentiate between fear (emotional) and arousal (somatic). People create fear (at the heart level) to try to control the stored somatic energies that seek a way to release and normalize. The fear of arousal causes ultimately depression and keeps the traumatic energies blocked. Levine says that emotional release alone would not heal trauma, it also takes somatic release. A non-judgmental or even appreciative, loving attitude toward any experience, emotional or somatic, is very important. Also, release without awareness won't do much good.

In very shorthand, I would say that somatic experiencing is a combination of focusing and regression plus repetitively ending the previously unfinished body intentions and releasing the stored body energy through any spontaneous body movement that comes up when contacting the incident (like jumping, shivering, crying, fist clenching etc.).

An experiment with Somatic Experiencing:

The last two days, I used myself as a 'guinea pig' and experimented a little bit with these ideas - which in Levine's book are more accurately described.

I found: It helps me to stay deliberately connected with my body experience rather than to dive into my emotions. It helped to massage my feet and hands to stay with my body experience. It's quicker and less emotionally stressful. (I did experience emotions when they came up, but I did not go for them.) I experienced a lot of shivering, snakelike movements, shaking, coolness and heat in my body, occasional tears and chaotic breathing. After the sessions I felt lighter and calmer than before. I feel more centered in my body.

During this experiment I did the other WHH steps, the phrase and the emotion, too, but I focused on the body's experience.

Conclusion:

From these experiments, it's getting really clear in my head that it is a body survival issue, not an emotional issue. I did a lot of emotional release work, but focusing on somatic release seems to be even more powerful. Many of those negative emotions like shame, guilt, anger, fear, sadness are the heart's way to try to control the unreleased body emotions. Many bodily pains and even heartbreaks ('emotional pain') are the body's signal that there are unreleased somatic energies.

A look at traditional techniques:

There are a lot of meditation and techniques around that focus on body experience, e.g. Kriya Yoga, Hatha Yoga, Mantak Chia's Tao Yoga, Tantric exercises, Yogananda's Energetization Exercises, or Progressive Relaxation. Their power, it seems, is derived from accessing and releasing stored body traumas in small steps."

EXERCISE—PRACTICE **WHH** AND **EFT** WITH A PARTNER

Try using WHH with EFT together. When might you not want to use the EFT part? Is it faster? What about ethical issues around using a therapy that can potentially come undone.

If you don't already know EFT, try and pick a partner who does, and switch off using it and not. Refer to Appendix D for a summary of the EFT process steps.

<u>Practice Session Notes:</u>

Practice Session Notes (continued):

SPECIAL TOPICS

Addictions

We've found quite an amazing result with addictions. In some cases DPR makes an addict, especially around alcohol, willing to heal the addiction. More experimentation is going on at this time. For current results, go to the Addiction Project page on the www.PeakStates.com website.

We've also seen cases where the addiction was caused by the influence a 'soul piece' had on the client.

> **Example:** The client was a woman in her thirties, who had been smoking since she was a preteen. After healing several traumas that she was using the smoking to suppress, she still wanted to smoke. This turned out to be caused by a 'soul piece' that wanted to smoke, and the client couldn't resist or change the feeling. She was able to detect it by realizing the desire to smoke was coming from what felt like someone else's personality. Using EFT on the feeling that she was holding onto this foreign feeling released the soul piece and the craving vanished.

We also seen several addictions caused by a 'hole' in people's chest. In one case, the client was using an addiction to relationships to cause the terrible emptiness of the hole to be covered. In several cases, I've seen smoking addictions caused by a hole in the chest. Generally, these holes were caused by physical injury to the chest in the birth canal. (Incidentally, healing this chest hole has consistently allowed the client to get conscious control over the heart chakra.)

Suicidal ideation

Suicidal clients need special attention and training, and a support place to be able to send them. Thus, I do NOT recommend that you work on these clients unless you are already a specialist in this area. Many people assume that it's just a loss of hope or interest in life that drives people to suicide, but this is not the case for the clients I've seen. There is actually a distinct and overwhelming feeling that makes a person want to kill themselves, even if they are too lethargic to do so.

There are three main problems with working with these clients:

- First, and most importantly, WHH (or any power therapy) will often heal the presenting problem in the first session. How could this be a bad thing? Because in many cases the problem is 'stacked', and there is more than one trauma, still hidden and not yet activated. If you didn't get them all, the following deadly problem can occur. Generally, the suicidal clients who have made it to your office are either fighting the feeling or feel too lethargic to actually act on their intention. After you heal the presenting trauma, they generally feel 'back to normal' and energized. If there are any more traumas with suicidal content in them, which get activated later outside of your office, the client now has the energy to actually kill themselves, instead of just thinking about it.

- If you don't heal the presenting suicidal feelings completely in the single office visit, you can easily make the problem worse. WHH activates the suppressed traumas, which are usually worse than the symptoms that have made it into the present. The clients can find themselves much more suicidal, leave your office, and kill themselves as the restraints they had inside themselves get overwhelmed.

- As we've determined that energy therapies can potentially be reversed, using them on a client who is suicidal is quite risky because of the chance that the healing can come undone later when they are not in a protected environment. This eliminates the most painless, fastest method to heal the problem, unfortunately.

What causes suicidal feeling to occur? In our limited exploration on this topic, we've found that it's related to the fetal baby's interactions with the placenta. The placenta has a limited self-awareness, which is supposed to die after birth. The baby's feelings about this, and the placenta's purpose get mixed together. Thus, suicidal feelings have tracked back to: the physical damage of cutting the umbilical; having the cord wrapped around the neck during birth; and the equivalent experience (second-hand, as it were) imprinted on the client's egg in the ovary in the mother during the mother's birth from the grandmother.

> **Example:** A woman in her early forties had suicidal feelings for months, and had been on medication without relief, trying suicide unsuccessfully a number of times. She recovered a birth trauma that was causing her symptoms, involving having the cord wrapped around her neck at birth. Although she continued medication, she no longer felt suicidal, instead energized and able to handle the pressing situations in her life. A week later, during a brief moment where she felt abandoned, she went into the garage and hung herself.

There is a chance that you or your clients, ones without any history of suicidal ideation, will become suicidal as a result of doing regressions. This can occur without you meaning to go to these kinds of traumas that have suicidal feelings. I highly recommend that you become familiar with this problem, as it may occur in your practice.

> **Example:** Probably due to my own inner exploration work, one day I suddenly became suicidal, a feeling I'd never had before. By accidentally touching my belly button three days later I suddenly realized the feelings were radiating from that spot. It turns out that this was due to the trauma of having my umbilical cord cut too soon.

> **Example:** A woman who was doing WHH by herself encountered traumas that made her feel like cutting her neck immediately and killing herself. She dealt with it by absolutely forbidding herself from moving from her couch until she'd dealt with the whole trauma. She had experienced slight suicidal feelings before doing regressive healing, but nothing as strong and immediate as this. In a later trauma involving her mom's birth, she found she could imagine a big light in her chest, and decide that this light was her higher self, and it was in charge of her healing. It made the suicidal feelings a whole lot less personal. As she puts it, "Your emotions are not you".

Stanislav Grof speaks about this sort of trauma in *The Holotropic Mind* (pg. 208), and I strongly suggest having a person who feels suicidal read this sort of material to get an intellectual understanding and some sort of hope to counteract these powerful feelings.

Suicidal ideation is also currently a category in the Spiritual Emergency experience list (see Appendix E). I have heard of cases where people ended up committing suicide partially due to the lack of understanding and support they experienced while they were going through what they and their intimates assumed were episodes of insanity. Doing our service as SEN volunteers keeps such tragedies from occurring. Suicidal ideation can also occur as spiritual emergencies activate early traumatic material.

Incidentally, at least for one client, the Inner Peace Process eliminated her suicidal feelings even though she didn't stay fully in the state afterwards. We're still exploring this surprising result of the process to see if she was unique, or if it's a common occurrence.

Depression

From mine and other practitioners' clinical experience, I've found the malady called depression is actually two similar but very different problems, all lumped under the same category. The first type is where the client has deep sadness, due to trauma, and basically can't feel much else. This type of 'depression' is quite easy to heal with any therapy that heals the originating trauma.

The second type is quite different. In that case, the client has the full range of emotions, but it's like they're very muted, and the best colloquial expression is that they 'have the blues'. The cause of this is not directly related to trauma, which is one reason why it doesn't respond well to WHH or EFT or most any other therapy.

It occurs when we have a thought stuck in our minds about something we just don't want to acknowledge. For example, a while after I was taught this I went into a deep depression. I spent three days not only depressed but also beating myself up because I couldn't find the thought I was hiding. As I walked along on the third day, I suddenly realized the thought was "I hate my Dad!" With that realization, the deep depression just vanished. I've never generated a simple way to find the depressive thought phrase, but if you do, please let me know so I can post it on the website.

Overlooked traumas

Further down the road on your healing journey, you may be used to healing those painful or difficult things that come up. However, watch for the following problem! You may find that it seems to you that what you are experiencing around some issue is normal, natural, and makes perfect sense. However, unless the feeling is accompanied by a sensation of peace, calm, and lightness simultaneously, you are actually just running a past trauma. This can be very tricky to notice at times, because often it seems that our response is justified from the circumstances! For example, one woman called me up feeling very angry after watching a TV show about the deaths of surplus children in China. She was convinced her feelings were justified, but she didn't feel that underlying calm I just mentioned. After she took a look, she discovered it was from her past, and her feeling about the TV show disappeared.

I'm emphasizing this point because a few people I've worked with really believed that what they were feeling was important to hang on to, permanently. In this example, the woman didn't want to stop being angry, because she had the idea that if she healed it, she would no longer care about the terrible things in the world that need to be changed. As tempting as this may seem, all that was really going on was that she was lost in the past, unable to respond appropriately to what's happening in her life and in the lives of the people around her. Similarly, another person had the idea that he had to hang on to his fear, else once his guard was down, something bad would happen to him. Again, his responses to what was really happening were laid down like a road. Sometimes it would work, but mostly he was blind to other options in his life - he'd keep repeating the same script over and over.

I want to really emphasize our mistaken beliefs about what is normal and natural in our emotional experiences. In another example, a man contacted me who was dying of cancer. He'd already lived past the time the doctors gave him, and he was terrified of dying. Since he didn't feel calm, peaceful, and light at the same time he was terrified, we knew it was something he could heal, although I had my doubts! After all, it seemed so reasonable! It turned out that his fear was actually coming from several incidents in the past, one I recall being a near drowning. Three weeks later he called me up, and said it was the strangest thing - he knew intellectually that he should be afraid, but he wasn't! (In case you're wondering, he survived his cancer.)

Body centered therapy as found in the book *At The Speed Of Life* by Hendricks can be useful in helping you spot the patterns that are driven by trauma but that you are unconscious of. Its only disadvantage is that it's tough to spot your own stuff, as it's so habitual it's hard to see. Working with one of their trained therapists once or twice is a good idea. They're used to doing extremely rapid healing, so it's by no means a waste of money.

Often, people have the experience that they've always felt a certain way, or that their home life as a child just had a certain atmosphere that couldn't be escaped. So when they work with me, they have the belief that there was no particular trauma that made them feel like they do. This is a mistake! True, they may have a lot of similar traumas, and they may have felt miserable in a certain way as long as they can remember, but it's always from specific moments, not some sort of long term soaking effect. Gay Hendricks and Frank Gerbode have come to this conclusion too.

I want you to particularly watch out for the idea that your mind heart, or body knows what's best. Phrases like "Use your head", "Trust your feelings", or "The body doesn't lie" turn out to be just not true. Unfortunately, by the time we get around to healing, every part of us is in delusion and generally pretty messed up. So, what can you trust? If you are not feeling that peace, calm and lightness that I continually talk about, you can be sure a trauma from your past is really doing all the talking. So, to really know the truth, you have to work whatever it is until you get to peace, then take a look. Another way to know that you are kidding yourself is to look at your life. Is it easy, fun, no problems? If you've got some problem, no matter how reasonable it looks, suspect that your past is getting in the way again. And finally, the big one for most people - anything that harms your physical body, no matter how reasonable it seems, is a delusion.

Another odd category of traumas is the one where the traumas feel good. I put this in this section on hidden trauma because you probably wouldn't be tempted to investigate them. To illustrate what I mean, one man recalled a feeling of strength and pride during an incident in grade school. However, this just meant that there was unreleased emotion, so he proceeded to drain the feeling in the normal manner. Underneath it to his great surprise was an extreme feeling of betrayal, and the rest of what really happened came into view.

Have you been plagued with silently talking to yourself, especially during meditation? Good news! This is driven by trauma that you can heal. It turns out that when you talk to yourself, you're actually talking to somebody else in the past. Just knowing this is usually enough to get you to find it. I do suspect that the origin for this type of trauma is trying to scream at our mother during womb or birth experiences, but I don't have enough data to know for sure. At any rate, healing this can sure make meditating more pleasant!

Do you constantly hear music in your head? This is often due to an association with a particular trauma, which is generally easy for the client to immediately recall when they look – the music and the trauma have the same 'feeling tone' to the person. (Occasionally the trauma is a developmental event, and the music one hears is similar to the 'spiritual' music that actually occurred during that event.) Another mechanism involves the mind storing the music (or voices or other sounds) exactly as they first occurred so it can replay it when it wants to – sometimes so it can use the content to manipulate the other brains. As I've mentioned elsewhere, this starts because it's a natural ability of the mind brain. However, it is a problem for the organism, causing a sort of 'jangle' internally when one tries to think. These 'recordings' can be eliminated by using a peak state called 'Inner Brightness' by 'seeing' them in the mind as lightly colored donut shaped rings, focusing on them, and allowing them to expand and dissolve. I don't yet know of a way to do this without that particular state.

Have you had a difficult time with someone in your life, a co-worker or anyone else? The idea that if we want someone to change, we have to change ourselves really works. Bringing all the material to light to heal it can be facilitated by using a trick of Alan Cohen's, the author of *The Dragon Doesn't Live Here Anymore*. In your imagination, embrace the difficult person while feeling love for them. Of course, most people find they just can't do it at first. However, trying allows you to flush up all the material from your past that needs healing. Alan reports that one of two things will happen when you're finally able to do it. Either the relationship will shift into a more harmonious one, or the other person will disappear from your life, as you end your part of the unconscious agreement you've made with them. I can report from my own experience that it worked just as he said it would! Incidentally, this same principle applies to positive affirmations. Rather than trying to drown out your feelings around some issue by repeating affirmations, I suggest using your resistance to them to flush up what needs to be healed.

There are other kinds of traumatic material I feel are too complex for the scope of this training level, but I'll end with some odd ones I've come across. For example, I'd unconsciously pretend I was an image I'd stored in my brain. Once in meditation I experienced myself become a roughly carved rock figure. It was a self-identity I picked up as a boy reading a book on archeology. The weirdest one I've seen so far was the experience of a large a glass palace in my head. This turned out to be an elaboration of my baby milk bottle - since it tasted good and didn't hurt, I envied it! I've also come across trauma's that blocked my memory ability, and others that blocked by ability to feel my emotions. Finally, in really severe trauma, I've relived experiences that felt like my brain (body, or heart) was being electrocuted. Well, good hunting!

Starting from the past—Trolling

For you high achiever types, trolling is what I call going into the past to heal a painful memory without starting from some problem in the present. Sort of like trolling for any fish that might be under there. This works fine, but has one major hidden problem - you have to take the time to see how this trauma is effecting you in the present, else you'll find the pesky thing just won't completely go away. With the normal procedure we don't have this problem, because you started from your misery in the present, and the connection is obvious. Also, don't forget to heal any other earlier memories that might arise. One other problem - if you try to heal it and quit before you finish, you might find that you suddenly have a new difficulty you didn't have before, as the pain you worked on erupts into the present. This really shows up when trolling for birth trauma! Occasionally I've had to heal other traumas connected with the trauma I trolled up, either before or after that moment, before I could bring myself to fully heal the one I started with. Again, this really shows up with birth trauma.

Dowsing

You may have read about people who dowse with rods or pendulums. It turns out that the people are actually communicating with their body consciousness when they get an answer the question. Applied kinesiology or muscle testing is an application of the same principle, although that is specifically geared for bodily injury, and generally used by chiropractors. However, you can use the same principles to ask your own body for information on your emotional and physical problems.

Finger dowsing as it's called works as follows. You are going to measure the strength of your muscles in order to find out what your body wants to say. It turns out that your body has the ability to strengthen or weaken muscles selectively, and you can use this to communicate with it. Make a circle by touching your thumb and ring (or little) finger. On your other hand, put your large middle finger and thumb together so that they touch, making a sort of arrow or needle shape. Put the needle shaped fingers into the circle shaped fingers. Then say out loud "Body, show me a yes", and pry your circled fingers apart with the stronger fingers that you were holding in the needle shape. Then, do it again while trying to hold your fingers at the same level of tightness, but say "Body, show me a no". You will generally find that a yes and no require quite different amounts of force to pry the fingers apart. If you don't get the expected result, switch hands. I've generally found that the hand you use the least is the best to measure muscular strength with.

This is a very powerful technique. By watching the strength of you fingers, you can use it to find out if the answer to your question is yes, no, maybe, or you've asked the wrong question. You can also ask for numerical data, by trying the choices one at a time, i.e. "Is it 1 day, 2 days", etc. It's also very handy if you've lost stuff, because you can, by a sort of 'hot and cold' procedure, find the item. But its use for us is in finding the traumatic origins to our current problems. You may have to use more than "20 questions", but it can really work, for example by asking "how old was I", "was Mom there", and so on. It's especially useful in physical problems, for choosing between different treatments, food allergy questions, supplements, and so on.

A variation on this is to try and feel resistance as you bring your hands together. If you can do this, the width of your hands indicate the yes or no answer. A woman I knew could use a left or right motion of her eyes, and there is of course the classical method of pendulums or dowsing rods. You can also do it with help by holding out your arm, and having someone else gently test the spring of your arm muscle by briefly pushing down on you arm. Incidentally, with all these techniques I recommend speaking out loud, or at least sub vocalizing. I suspect that typically it's hard for the body to figure out what question the brain is asking without doing this.

However, this is not magic (although it may seem like it at times). Your body consciousness is still you, and if your body has a counter commitment to telling the truth, you're going to get lies. Or you might get made up answers, a sort of "I'll be helpful even if I have to make it up". It turns out that this suffers from problems that other psychic techniques do, but on the other hand sometimes it can really work well. Suspicion, discrimination and reality checking are the keys here. Dowsing can also be used to help others, but this is fraught with pitfalls, and is much more problem filled than just dowsing for yourself.

Finally, certain questions will get different answers depending on your state of consciousness. For example, if you ask "Will I heal faster if I practice loving myself, and how much faster?", I've found that you actually have to go into the state of consciousness you're asking about to get valid results.

Rape

To my surprise, there is a common core trauma experience to the rape survivors I've seen, especially ones who have been raped multiple times. After regression, it has always led (so far any rate) to the birth trauma. Apparently, the fetus experiences the mother in the same way the adult experiences the perpetrator - strong sexual feeling, physically strong and unyielding. The tricky part here is in realizing that not only is it a replay of the unyielding womb wall, but that there is a sex change (given that the survivor is female and the perpetrator is male) from the present circumstances to the womb experience.

Merging with the client

It is possible not only to experience directly what a client is feeling, but it's possible to heal it directly also. However, healing your client directly is beyond the scope of the class, but is taught in the advanced WHH class. We do NOT recommend you try this on your own, because it has a potential problem of occasionally inducing schizophrenia type symptoms in the therapist. Training is required to avoid this problem, and in fact it is the first process we teach our advanced WHH students.

However, there are a few little tricks you can use that don't have the same problem. When working with a client, especially when they are ignoring you, very upset and oblivious, or resistant, there is a cute trick that sometimes works. Look at them not as the adult in the room with you at the present, but instead allow yourself to see them as the child they have become at that moment as the old trauma takes them over. Often, this has the affect that suddenly they start paying attention to you, and you can go from there. The effect can be quite remarkable. It also works in everyday situations also.

Another very cute trick is to put your attention on your client while they're working on their trauma. As you do so, focus your attention simultaneously on your own head, heart, and belly. You may find that there is a stiffness, or rigidity, between the areas of the body (diaphragm, throat) or in the areas themselves. Feel into that rigidity and ask yourself, what position is that brain holding that keeps it from merging with the other brains? It's just like working with a little kid who is upset and wants to take his marbles and go home. When you can feel the reason for the upset, it allows the brain to release its position and merge into the rest of the being. As this happens, the client will suddenly find that their trauma will release. Even though it felt like you were working on yourself at the time!

EFT and TAT both can be used to heal a client without their participation. Called surrogate healing, the therapist tap themselves, or hold the TAT pose while they focus on the client. It often works, but I suspect that caution would be advised in case this process causes the therapist to pick up the client's issue. Too, there are ethical issues involved around healing a person without their permission that need to be addressed by the practitioner.

Key Points:

- WHH can be used for a variety of unusual psychological and physical problems once the indirect connection to trauma is understood, and healed there.

- Muscle testing, applied kinesiology, or dowsing can give valid information, but can't be trusted because it can also give invalid information. Surrogate testing has an even worse reliability.

SPIRITUAL EMERGENCIES

(see Appendix F for a description of categories of spiritual emergencies.)

Spiritual emergencies are not crises of faith. Instead, they involve very disruptive and disturbing episodes of experiences that are outside of our cultural belief systems. Often, people have these sorts of spiritual experiences without major upsets in their lives, but for some people the experiences are too abrupt and extreme for the person to deal with. When these spiritual experiences become a crisis, it's called a spiritual emergency.

> **Example:** One man had a deep spiritual awakening when he suddenly experienced the unity of all mankind. This was fine except that it was so sudden and extreme that he decided to run naked down the main street of town telling everyone how amazingly wonderful they were! (He was hauled to the local mental hospital, where a psychiatrist recognized the state and just kept him there till he regained his balance between this tremendous insight and the need to function in the world. It could have been a tragedy, if he'd been dosed with anti psychotic medications for something that had nothing to do with psychosis.)

> **Example:** A woman had a sudden 'psychic opening', finding that she could 'hear' other people's thoughts. She couldn't shut it off, and found the whole experience disturbing and quite frightening at first.

A number of clients you will probably see in the future are suffering from a spiritual emergency. This is because of a very interesting transpersonal reason. As soon as you become comfortable with an area (such as sexual abuse, spiritual emergency, etc.), you suddenly start getting that type of client. (When the client is mirroring your unhealed material, you tend to see those people consistently right from the beginning of your work.) A list of the common ones categorized by Dr. Stanislav Grof are given in Appendix E, but there are actually a number of experiences not covered in his categories, unfortunately. I recommend taking classes and reading any of a number of good books on the subject of spiritual emergencies. In the section below, I cover a few of the emergency categories that I have original contributions to, but this coverage is far from complete. See Appendix E for the rest.

The tools you'll be learning in this class are often very useful for your clients in this type of crisis. In particular, since WHH often brings up spiritual experiences of a huge variety, it's valuable to be able to recognize them so you won't be trying to fix a client who actually doesn't have a problem!

For a referral center and source for current material on this topic, I recommend looking at the Spiritual Emergence Network (SEN) website which is maintained at the California Institute for Integral Studies in their Psychology Master's program.

Unitive experiences: Fusion, the Beauty Way, and Wholeness

We will first look at a group of experiences which fall under Grof's spiritual emergence category of unitive consciousness. Although rare, these remarkable states occur when two or more of the brains fuse (merge) together. Even greater states of unitive experience occur when the person also merges with transpersonal awarenesses, but this is outside the scope of the basic WHH class. In fact, total fusion of the three brains into one awareness is our normal state as we develop in the womb. However, by birth the trauma we've each experienced has created the disassociation of the brains which we consider 'normal', and we spend the rest of our lives unconsciously searching for this internal fusion in our outer lives. Even though these fusion states are intrinsically positive and in themselves do not create a spiritual emergency, when people lose these peak states they sometimes contact SEN, often expressing confusion, grief and despair as they search for some way to regain the state they've lost.

The most common of these states involves head and heart fusion. Probably the most well know of the states that have this fusion is 'The Beauty Way', from the American Indian tradition, or 'aliveness' as Harville Hendrix does in *Keeping the Love You Find*, or 'an awareness of the Immanent Divine', from the Christian tradition. This state has the unique property that past emotional trauma no longer has an emotional effect on people, and they find themselves totally in the present. It may have lasted only briefly or for most of a lifetime, but during it they feel vividly alive, and everything around them feels vividly alive too. In a certain way, everything is beautiful, even garbage, and even painful emotions feel satisfying. However, people in this state know they are not perfect, and they still have problems interpersonally and in their lives. When they lose this state, they tend to call SEN because they now miss a knowledge of spiritual truths that seemed perfectly obvious during the experience, and so assume it must have something to do with spiritual states. Often, they've attempted to find what they've lost from spiritual groups or teachers but their experience has met without recognition and dismissed as unimportant. (Consciously letting go of judging people has brought some into this state. Another method, that has even worked for people that have never experienced mind and heart fusion before, is to consciously face all the subtle reasons that you have for not being fully in the present. This usually takes a few days and outside help.)

A variety of other peak states can occur and become a crisis when they are lost. For example, ones giving a feeling of happiness, of having no skin boundary, of being hollow like a empty tin can, of being whole, and so on. For complete descriptions and causes of these states, refer to our *Peak States of Consciousness Volumes 1 and 2*.

Reassuring someone that you've heard about what they describe is very supportive and helpful. The Institute has developed methods to get peak states of consciousness, and a variety of others do also. See Appendix H for a list of processes from other groups. For people who have lost a fusion state, if they can spot the circumstances that caused them to leave fusion, a variety of trauma healing techniques can be used to eliminate the traumatic memory that had been activated. For further reading on the topic of fusion as well as other peak states of consciousness, I refer you to Tom Brown Jr.'s *The Quest* and *Awakening Spirits*. Advanced WHH focuses on these and other peak states of consciousness.

At the end of the basic WHH training, you'll have the choice on whether you'd like to run through a process that may give you one of these brain fusion states relatively permanently.

Turning the brains off: Shutdown, Samahdi, and The Pearl Beyond Price

A much stranger set of states, still sometimes put in the category of unitive consciousness, can occur because the individual brains have the seldom used ability to turn themselves off. During these states, the person looses the abilities that were primary to those brains. This generally occurs due to what that individual experiences as extreme trauma, or sometimes from spiritual practices. Interestingly, we don't lose our ability to use language when these shutdown states occur.

The state that occurs when the mind (cortex) shuts down has no particular name that I'm aware of, but it presents a very seductive yet problem filled situation. The person experiences a sense of peace, calmness, feelings of simple joy in living and doing everyday tasks, a connection to spiritual writings that is very profound. This occurs because internal conflicts the person experiences due to the independent actions of the mind cease. However, the abilities that the mind specialize in, short term memory, mathematical ability, and the ability to form judgments (such as choosing between similar items in a store, or making a menu choice) are also suspended or greatly impaired. This internal lobotomy presents a real dilemma, as the individual wants the state to continue, but find themselves unable to work at most jobs. I've seen people stay this way for as long as a year.

The next state is called samahdi in the Zen Buddhist tradition. Here, both the heart and the body consciousnesses turn themselves off. One experiences a sense of peace and timelessness that is beyond anything possible to experience in normal consciousness. The person finds themselves almost never breathing, probably because the need for oxygen metabolism to support the chemically based thinking processes of the two shutdown brains is eliminated. Unlike the previous state, the individual can continue to work at most jobs, and in fact the memory and IQ is extremely enhanced. (One odd problem with this state is the ability to recall what we hear, such as music or conversation, so clearly it cannot be distinguished from the real thing. We can go into a state of continuous playback, but turning the playback off can be difficult.) Unfortunately, the ability to feel emotions, or connect with people other than intellectually is eliminated. Once in the state, the person can remain in it indefinitely. The desire to experience feelings again is a trigger to ending this by turning on the heart, and the body consciousness soon follows.

When we turn off both the mind and the heart, we are left with a state the Sufis call an experience of the 'Pearl Beyond Price'. This odd state is similar to fusing the mind and body in that we experience ourselves as if we were made of air, without a boundary at the skin. Unlike fusion, in this state our lower belly feels as if it were full, a bit like we'd eaten a large meal or were pregnant. We also lose the abilities of the heart and mind, such as being able to feel emotions, be emotionally aware of others, think analytically, and so on. Spiritual practice accompanied by feelings of dying and trying to escape our lives can trigger this state.

The previous three cases generate calls to SEN because of the 'spiritual' overtones to the experiences, and from the dilemma people face in trying to decide if they should go back to the cacophony of three independent brains. As a helper, it is useful to point out that lobotomizing oneself to avoid pain is probably not in their best interest, and discussing how to heal trauma and live with more self-love as an alternative is a key step. Simply desiring the aspects of themselves that have been turned off is usually sufficient to end these shutdown states.

Kundalini Awakening

Quite a number of calls I receive have to do with this category of spiritual emergency. Although a variety of transpersonal experiences are associated with kundalini, the basic triune brain model directly addresses the part of the kundalini experience that causes so much pain and suffering for people, the activation of old traumatic memories. The standard practice of first reassuring them that the phenomenon is real, recommending books to read on the subject, and discussing it's potential course is very helpful. But beyond this, I usually recommend a variety of ways, mentioned at the end of the article, to heal trauma so they can directly deal with the problems that are suddenly disrupting their lives.

The definitive classic kundalini symptom is that of a small area of heat, the size of a silver dollar, rising up the spine usually over a period of weeks or more. As it rises, it triggers traumas energetically associated with those areas of the body. Often kundalini is accompanied by sensations of being frantic and disoriented. A simple temporary solution is to have the person stretch their arm out in front of them, and then move it in an infinity symbol (a figure eight on it's side), while holding the head facing forward without moving. By following their upright thumb with their eyes, so that the thumb is seen first by one eye, then the other in a smooth motion causes the anxiety to lift in seconds. Supposedly this causes the hemispheres of the brain to start working in synchronization again, but I don't know if this is the correct reason or not.

I want to mention something else about this phenomenon I hope will spur investigation by other people. During my own kundalini experience, I did some deep psychological work, and found that I was experiencing kundalini because my body consciousness was essentially blaming the other two brains for all it's problems. My body was pretending that by harming itself through the disruption caused by kundalini it would fix things, with a getting even at the other brains sort tone to it. However, once I faced the pain around this delusion, my kundalini experience immediately ended. Of course, I don't know if this is commonly the case for others, but it was certainly a surprise to me and well worth further investigation.

I have observed that in spite of what some spiritual literature says, many people have years of kundalini experiences with little or no observable benefits, and this may explain why—the core problem is not being addressed.

Psychological Renewal Through Activation of the Central Archetype

I haven't worked with anyone having this experience, yet I have come across something similar in my own work that I would like to share that may be useful. During a holotropic breathwork session and for quite a while afterwards, I experienced an episode of being in the middle of a world shattering conflict between two tremendous beings or archetypal forces. Investigating further revealed the core of the experience was part of the birth trauma, where my body consciousness was contending with my mother's body consciousness for what I felt was my survival during the hellish conditions of birth. This experience had the sensation of two gods contending because the body consciousness feels like a god to the other two brains, as one might expect given that biologically the body consciousness is primary and the other brains genetically designed as extensions to it.

I've had a chance to test out this understanding in a few clients who were experiencing this emergency and it tuned out to also be true for them.)

Possession, Schizophrenia, and Channeling

Years ago as a SEN helper I was taught that true spiritual emergencies are short term and result in higher functioning individuals after the crisis passes, and that they generally happen to mentally healthy people, probably as a developmental step (see Appendix A). In contrast, real mental illness was categorized as somehow not spiritual, as it was more devastating, permanent, the realm of therapists and drugs, and by implication hopeless. Yet I couldn't help but notice that, for example, very disruptive kundalini and channeling experiences were occurring in people over a period of decades, and that they did not appear to be benefiting in any obvious way from them. I've come to reject that SEN model, and in this section I'll be specifically addressing the connection between the mental illness called schizophrenia, the controversial SEN category called possession, and the trendy phenomenon of channeling. I'll finish by briefly describing ways to heal these problems.

First, these three phenomena are actually manifestations of the same underlying mechanism. It turns out that our bodies have the ability to pull in and hang onto other people's soul pieces, which in shamanic terms is called 'soul stealing'. These pieces are popularly called 'entities' or 'angels' depending on the emotional tone they carry from their formation. Unlike our own trauma pieces which we can erase or modify with certain psychological approaches, we apparently cannot do this to ones from other people, nor can we ignore them as easily. Unconsciously doing soul stealing is actually fairly common among 'normal' people, and is something a shamanic practitioner deals with all the time.

How these soul pieces affect us depends on a number of factors, such as how hard we resist the 'playback' process, how many soul pieces we're dealing with, how intense and what primary emotion each piece contains, how often we're triggered into playback, are we blocking the verbal content of the playback process, and so on. Thus, the condition we call schizophrenia is actually an extreme and disruptive case of uncontrollable play back of one or more of these stolen soul pieces. Likewise, in my limited experience the controversial SEN category of possession is an even more intense version of the same process, where the trauma piece(s) involved are extremely negative and dramatic. Finally, the popular practice of channeling is also a manifestation of the same mechanism, albeit done with more control and less mental disruption. This last assertion can be difficult for people doing channeling to accept, especially since people would like to believe that they have a connection to sources of higher wisdom. I'd always been skeptical about channeling after looking at the functional usefulness of what was said, but I became downright suspicious when I noticed that channeling caused minor harm to peoples' bodies during the experience, a flag to me that some sort of psychological self deception was going on.

However, I wasn't absolutely sure until I'd worked out the mechanism, and a way to heal it, and had a chance to test it. Of course, it's always possible that more than one type of channeling exists, but so far every individual who I've worked with has been doing what I described. (For complete references to the entire channeling phenomenon, I refer you to the excellent books by John Klimo or Arthur Hastings.)

So, why would anyone do this to themselves, which in the extreme can even cause you to harm others or drive you crazy? Many healers (and Hollywood movies) have the viewpoint that somehow people are the victims of nasty or confused entities or lost souls who wonder around looking for somebody whose defenses are down so they can move in. Realizing that we are actually the perpetrators, not the victims, doing this to ourselves by grabbing and holding on to soul pieces is hard to believe (if you can accept this stuff at all) until you understand why. The reason is actually hidden in birth and womb trauma, which is why so few people find it. During birth, and occasionally in the womb, our body consciousness associates survival with the sensation of being surrounded by the emotion(s) our mother felt at those moments. This is similar to the sensation we get when we pull in an external soul piece, and so at a deeply unconscious level we are convinced that to survive we have to hang onto it no matter what. In fact, we also tend to seek out people who feel those particular emotions much of the time for the same reason. Thus, healing soul stealing has the benefit of fixing two problems at once. A complete description of the process can be found in our books *Silencing the Voices* and *Peak States of Consciousness, Volume 3*.

We can heal soul stealing in several other ways. For example, the Hanbleceya care facility in southern California uses a body centered approach which routinely heals schizophrenia, albeit slowly. In this approach, they bring the person to an awareness that they are causing themselves to be schizophrenic, and some time later they bring the person to the decision to stop doing it. If possible, I prefer any of a variety of trauma healing techniques that access birth and womb memories. This usually is very rapid, usually less than a couple of hours. Another method is to have a shaman remove the soul piece causing the problem, and although I've seen this approach work, I don't know if it eliminates the underlying survival issue for a permanent cure. Probably the most pleasant way to block the phenomenon, although it doesn't cause us to give up the soul pieces, is to go into mind and heart fusion (Inner Peace). In this state, we no longer play back trauma pieces, including ones we pull in from outside.

Incidentally, accessing past (or future) lives can result in an experience that resembles channeling, but I suspect this is done extremely rarely. See the discussion on past lives for more information.

At least as of this writing, the soul-piece stealing problem appears to be the dominant mechanism for the problems of possession, schizophrenia, and channeling. However, other potential mechanisms exist. For example, I've seen people who occasionally have a part of their body (such as an arm) apparently move by it's own volition. Another may find themselves repeating a certain word uncontrollably, perhaps a swear word. In the extreme, I've met people who feel that they are occasionally completely 'taken over' by the sensation of some overwhelming being or energy. These people experience this as completely outside their control and very frightening or disturbing. They find they cannot block or resist it in spite of all their efforts. I suspect that it is possible for the body consciousness to briefly gain partial control of the organism to play out delusional material it's holding due to some trauma. Since the other triune brains generally experience the body consciousness as a godlike being, when one accidentally perceives the body consciousness from their perspective it can leading to the misidentification of the real cause of the problem. Of course, this mechanism can manifest positively especially in the absence of any delusional traumatic material, as for example when someone suddenly find extremes of strength to save a life, or to suddenly heal oneself of some illness, or to experience themselves as an almost archetypal sexual being during lovemaking. Other mechanisms for these symptoms involve purely transpersonal, archetypal forces, and can be treated by addressing the fear and resistance to this type of internal experience.

Hauntings, Ghosts, and Psychic Attacks

Although not strictly spiritual emergency, some SEN calls are requests for help and understanding around experiences involving haunting, ghosts, or psychic attacks. It turns out that many of these experiences are another expression of the soul piece phenomenon, and can be dealt with in several ways.

I was pretty skeptical about 'ghosts' until I ran into this phenomenon myself. About a year after the death of my mother, and as a result of some inner work I was doing, I suddenly felt like I was being crushed. I grew aware that my mother was 'present' and trying to communicate. After some work, I found she wanted me to make a promise, upon which she vanished. The issue was about my brother and dad's health, which she'd felt a lot of despair around when she was alive. This type of communication doesn't normally come up in with the basic WHH process, but it can be done deliberately using the advanced techniques. For people in 'average' consciousness who want to communicate with dead relatives and friends, I recommend Dr. Raymond Moody's book *Reunions*. He has a very simple way to have people communicate with the dead as if they were actually, physically still present.

A number of clients have described a very uncomfortable feeling of someone's presence nearby, watching them or threatening them. The clients are not mentally ill, and are in an average state of consciousness. This mechanism involves another person unconsciously constructing a soul piece with an imprint of themselves and their desire, ejecting it from the body field, and using it to try and either defend themselves, attack others, or to try and get their way. The piece has the sense of the creator's personality in it, and can be seen as a person or as a black cloud in various peak states of consciousness. The key here is to realize that our body consciousness actually pulls the piece to us at an energetic level, even if it causes us fear. Using EFT on the idea that we're pulling this to ourselves often solves the problem quickly. Using WHH in the 'Silent Mind' technique is a permanent, albeit slower solution.

Thus, one doesn't even have to be dead to create a 'ghost' of ourselves! And in fact, it's a very common phenomenon. I wouldn't wonder if this soul piece creation process isn't the basis of some so called black magic practices, as well as the origin of some of the so-called 'angels' being channeled.

> **Example:** A 35 year old woman created a piece as a result of trauma involving abandonment. She would unconsciously use it to defend herself from men who she felt were about to leave her, giving them a very eerie sensation of a threatening presence. Gently confronting the woman on this issue caused her to pull it back in and face her trauma around abandonment.

> **Example:** In my own case, I found I'd created a piece due to a trauma involving trying to protect myself from being spanked by my dad which was interfering with dowsing that one of my teachers was trying to do for me. And even more seriously, I'd created a soul piece as a result of the birthing process to 'attack' women who reminded me of my threatening mother. Healing the generating trauma, something that happened when I was less than a year old, caused the pieces to be pulled back in with a 'pop' sensation, and dissolved.

There are other mechanisms beside soul pieces that can be lumped under the category of 'psychic attacks'. This material is beyond the scope of this manual but is covered in the advanced work. This sort of thing happens all the time, because people use natural human abilities in unconscious ways. Normally, people are not affected by these attacks, but some people are vulnerable because of trauma in certain pre-birth developmental events, which cause them to lose natural immunity. However, I want you to understand that this problem does exist for some people, and that there are several different mechanisms lumped in this category that can create actual, physical symptoms in clients. If you find a client has a physical issue that doesn't appear to be trauma related, you might want to refer them to someone who has training in this area, or get training yourself.

Shamanic Crisis

Several excellent books on the shamanic journey experience and other elements of the shamanic crisis can be readily found now, such as Harner's classic *The Way of the Shaman*. However, I do want to mention one aspect of the shamanic experience I think it is important for SEN helpers to at least have heard about that is not generally found in the literature. I became familiar with this phenomenon by accident during a holotropic breathwork session while I was exploring the pain around having self-identities. When I dissolved the earliest one that my body held (a delusion of being my father acquired during the birth trauma), I experienced a sensation of sacredness and suddenly my body awareness became radically different. Repeating this process in turn with the other two brains, I found myself changed to such an extent I experienced myself as something totally unfamiliar, without any similarity to the human identity I call myself.

I've since been able to do this from ordinary consciousness, and it appears that to my surprise that each of my brains has a counterpart or extension in some other sort of 'realm'. It's difficult to describe, but I get a 'visual' impression of fluorescent blackness, timeless, and a sensation of being a bit as if I resembled something a totem pole might be trying to portray. Incidentally, I was comfortably aware of this duality while in the womb. The only reference to this state of consciousness that I'm aware of is in *The Vision* and *Awakening Spirits* by Tom Brown Jr., a shamanically trained westerner. He refers to it as 'The Realm of the Shaman'. In my limited experience this state of being is part of the key to regenerative healing, and is certainly a fascinating aspect of the human psyche.

Death and Dying

The grief due to the death of someone can be a devastating experience. But particularly in cases involving a death due to one's own actions, either real or imagined, the burden can be beyond belief. As a SEN helper, I can suggest a technique, which apparently allows most people to directly communicate face to face with the dead person, generally a family member, in order to come to resolution on their issues. Rediscovered from a process used by the ancient Greeks by Dr. Raymond Moody, it was described in his book Reunions, and is gaining popularity, albeit slowly. From a therapeutic standpoint it appears very useful. Amazingly enough, in around 80% of the clients, the 'spirits' of the dead come to the client and communicate with them. Occasionally, my clients access a connection to the Creator where they can communicate 'verbally' with the dead. I mention this hear because you might have a client experience this when using WHH.

> **Example:** A woman grieving over the death of a very loved elderly woman, a shaman. We used a trauma healing technique on her grief, and tracked it back to the birth stage before crowning. Her mother had been told to keep her legs together to stop the birthing until the doctor could arrive. After healing this trauma, her grief over the death completely vanished and did not return. Interestingly, she reported that her deceased friend could now communicate directly with her (even though she was now dead). Apparently the grief blocked her communication with her student. Truth or delusion? I don't know, but I do know that this is possible, even if this particular client was only kidding herself.

Past Lives

The issue of past lives can come up for people calling SEN in a number of ways. The memory may have surfaced due to a past life regression, during trauma healing work, or spontaneously. In general, the caller requires reassurance that this phenomenon has occurred for others, and references to one of the many excellent books on the subject can be made. However, in my experience one problem that can occur for SEN helpers is to assume that just recalling the past life is adequate to heal it. Since the individual usually has a tremendous sense of relief when he recalls the memory and sees why this life has had problems because of it, it is easy to jump to this conclusion. Unfortunately, the trauma needs to be healed just like any trauma does in their current lifetime.

At the risk of losing credibility, deeper levels of the past life experience can occur especially among people doing spiritual practices, and I feel SEN helpers should at least have heard of this even if they don't believe it. Normally, we think of the past as fixed, and the future as yet to form. However, imagine for a moment that our 'spirit' exists forever, and can have a viewpoint outside of time from which it sees that all events past and future have already occurred. However, change is possible because individuals can shift their awareness, or 'spirit', through time and act on what will have or has already occurred. Thus, one can have the experience of interacting with ones past life or future life to change events. In fact, one can actually give oneself advice and guidance from one lifetime to the next, the ultimate example of raising oneself by lifting one's own bootstraps! An excellent example of this phenomenon can be found in Hank Wesselman's *Spiritwalker*. Since most of us can hardly run our own current life, let alone another's, I generally don't encourage this practice.

At this point, it appears that traumatic incidents are carried from the past into the present because our natural, untraumatized state is to be connected simultaneously with all our previous and future lives. When we return to heal these trauma we can view those lives by translating our 'spiritual' viewpoint into the actual past, and we get the odd sensation of recognizing ourselves and others even though we have a different personality and body in that life.

Key Points:

- A variety of spiritual experiences exist. Knowledge of them is important for the outcome of the therapy session to be positive for the client.

- Power therapies, especially WHH, can evoke spiritual experiences. Be sure to acknowledge the reality of what the clients are going through, as they often need the validation of these foreign experiences.

EXERCISE—PRACTICE WHH ON SPECIAL TOPICS WITH A PARTNER

Feel free to work with one of the special topics that you've just gone over. Or any other issue that feels important to you. The key here is practice, practice, practice, so that when you leave the class you'll feel comfortable in actually using this process.

Practice Session Notes:

Practice Session Notes (continued):

QUIZ #3

1. What do you tell a client to do who encounters a 'wire' or 'bottle' in their body during healing a trauma?

2. Do you have to heal the correct trauma first before you can get a soul piece back?

3. What alternatives do you have if the client won't sing a song?

4. If, during a healing, the client describes a cloud coming out of their bodies, what does this mean and what do you do?

5. If, during a healing, the client describes seeing their own body walking away from them while they're still in their body in the trauma in the past, what does this mean and what do you do?

6. When is it appropriate to use a mixture of EFT and WHH with a client? Or just EFT?

7.   When is it not appropriate to use EFT or energy therapy with a client?

8.   What is the presenting symptom that we suspect often hides the ability to open and use the heart chakra?

9.   What do you do for a generational trauma?

10. For some clients, where do they feel the generational trauma comes from (a physical direction)?

11. When is it especially useful to use the TIR 'viewing' of a traumatic sequence? (2 examples)?

12. Is the phenomenon of physical or emotional 'shock' a problem with WHH?

13. Is WHH an energy, meridian, or other kind of therapy?

14. Is depression a symptom of trauma?

15. Is muscle testing reliable for trauma work?

16. Can TAT be permanent? Or is it reversible?

17. Are holes in people common or uncommon?

18. What are two ways people can harm or block each other from healing, but at a distance?

19. Do meridian therapies heal holes?

20. When using EFT or other meridian therapy on a client's headaches, and they come back after a while, what does this mean and how do you fix it?

21. Why do we believe that the healing from using meridian therapies is potentially reversible?

22. When doing DPR, is it OK to say "In fact, it's the client's problem that makes them so lovable, and in fact if they didn't have it they wouldn't be so lovable?"

Day 4

CLIENTS NOT TO WORK WITH

This is a cautionary message for any of you who are thinking about working with certain types of clients: ritual abuse survivors; sexual abuse survivors (especially parent incest); suicidal clients; domestic violence clients; and clients with global trust issues. DON'T! Many of you are not trained as therapists, or even if you are you require specialized experience to handle these types of clients. There are probably other categories that I can't think of right now, but these are the biggies. PLEASE learn these techniques on 'easy' clients; I'm starting to get ulcers!!

If you are working with non-family members, please familiarize yourselves with support resources that you can send your clients to if you uncover this sort of thing. Or take the specialized training, and I have recommendations for excellent ones if you want to pursue this. Regardless, you ESPECIALLY need to find out where to send clients if they get suicidal. This has big legal consequences, and you need to respect your limitations and your client's safety.

1. **Clients with heart or other potentially fatal physical conditions:** WHH can bring up intense physical issues and emotional pain, and so a possibility exists that this work can trigger a heart attack in someone with a weak heart. Of course, this is true of a number of other therapies, but be careful! Check to see if your clients have this sort of problem, as they may not think to tell you.

2. **Ritual abuse or 'satanic' cult survivors:** First of all, these groups exist, and you might get clients who have grown up as victims of this stuff, usually children of members. Send them to specialists in this area! These clients have tremendous amounts of severe problems, and you don't have the time or experience to handle them. I've heard some of my colleagues doubt the existence of this sort of thing, but it exists. If these groups let someone survive this sort of thing, and the survivor goes to a therapist, the groups tend to get worried and often threaten or kill the therapist. THIS MIGHT BE YOU! THIS IS BEYOND YOUR LEVEL OF EXPERTISE, so leave it to specialists who work with the police in this area. If you have someone in this category, I can refer them to folks I know are good in this area.

3. **Sexual Abuse Survivors:** Again, these clients really require specialized training. I know we've all seen Gary Craig heal incest on stage, but his clients are functional enough to come to the workshop, tend to be therapists themselves, etc. In your office you can get anything. So, why are these a problem? First, you need the experience of being around survivors who are reexperiencing the full horror of the situation, so that it won't affect you. Else you unconsciously limit what is OK for the client to feel. This experience is not something that you pick up naturally; its very gruesome and shocking to see a number of people go through this experience. (Incidentally, this applies to torture victims also, as in governmental prisons like in Greece or South America.) Second, if they don't get through the particular experience that you are working on, and if it is a memory that they've just recovered, they may go out and try and kill the perpetrator. Or they suffer horribly between sessions. Third, this stuff can bring up suicidal feelings, and if you don't heal it and know what to do, they can kill themselves (see below). Fourth, using 'arithmetic' level healing techniques such as power therapies, you need experience and practice in helping the client bring up these horrible memories if they are repressed. Else, your client can walk out of your office feeling horrible for long periods of time and not know why - and blaming you to boot for 'doing' something to them.

Another reason to not work with these folks - whatever your gender, you can trigger all kinds of stuff just by being that gender, and the client has a hard time working with you. Even if they are OK with you for a while, they may need to work with the opposite gender therapist at other times. For example, say a man was raped by his father as a baby (a real example, he was only 11 months old when it started). He typically had father stuff, but mother stuff would come around her not defending him. A two gender team is the most successful in these cases.

4. **Suicidal clients:** These need specialists, even if the specialists use standard techniques that are useless. First, the legal ramifications are tremendous. If they kill themselves while under your care, you can be sued or put in prison if you are not licensed. For that matter, you can be sued by them or relatives anyway for not being licensed even if they don't die. Second, they can take a tremendous, 24 hour 7 day a week kind of care from you if you start with them, and this can go on for months or years. You don't have this sort of time. Leave this to others who want to take this on. Second, if you are working with them, they might feel they don't have to work with anyone else, and this is not the case. They often need to be in 24 hour watch facilities so that they don't take their lives while doing the healing work. Third, you don't know the medications that can be only prescribed by specialists, and although I hate them—they sometimes do help keep your client alive until you can fix them. This area is for people who are trained in it, please leave it to them.

    Let me give you a horrible personal example. I've only been in love once in my entire life. Years later, this woman showed up again during an episode of separation with her husband, feeling suicidal. She had been having an affair, and her husband said it was "him or me." She was addicted to sex with the other guy, so her husband started divorce proceedings. This led to her feeling intensely suicidal. She had slashed her wrists, and barely survived (it usually coagulates, but there are ways around that). She'd overdosed on pills, and again barely made it. She was under the care of a psychiatrist who was dosing her with medication, but the suicidal feelings continued of course. She came to me, and we did a piece of birth trauma. She left feeling energized for the first time in months. However, a few days later, an earlier piece came up (notice my insistence that you need to go all the way to the core) while she was home, and she hung herself.

    Two things to note here. First, suicidal stuff has its origins in the womb. Thus, to be successful, you need to have healed enough womb stuff to make it easy for your clients. Suicidal stuff is particularly difficult for non-suicidal people to access, and needs to be done on purpose with somebody who has been through it already. In the work I did with her, we had not gotten to the original trauma, (she'd had enough for the day) but she didn't come back in time to finish. If I'd been working with her in a facility, this would not have happened. Often, the suicide repeats the sensation they had while *in utero* that drives the suicide, and in this case she had a trauma about the cord being wrapped around her neck during birth. Third, suicidal people don't often take their lives while they're in the depths of it, they feel too rotten and lethargic to do it. Instead, they tend to kill themselves after some work or good experiences gives them enough energy so that they can actually carry out their original intentions. So your help can set them up to die. Enough said.

5. **Domestic violence clients:** This situation is also for specialists and the police. The one being abused finds that they cannot leave, even as the abuse escalates to the point that they are hospitalized, and eventually killed. There is a profile for the abuser that points to the likelihood that they will kill their spouse, but it's statistical in nature, and so in this situation you should figure it is possible with anyone. If you get involved, you're only giving the illusion of safety to them (after all, they go home after you see them), and hence are doing them a great disservice that might lead to their deaths. Second, the abusive spouse will likely come after you, because (s)he is just as addicted to abusing the victim as the victim is addicted to being abuse. And neither really want to end it at a deep level. I could say more here, but I hope you get the message. Yes, you might be able to break the cycle in one healing session, but you might also not, and that could be disastrous. So, leave it to experts, or get the appropriate training yourself.

6. **Global trust issues:** Avoid these clients for a different reason. These are the clients who come to you talking about how their previous therapist was untrustworthy, didn't help them, asking about your qualifications, and in general giving you the idea that they are excessively suspicious or untrusting. There are several reasons. First, no matter how good a job you do eliminating their problem, they will not be satisfied. They will go out and tell the world that you are untrustworthy, incompetent, etc, etc just as they told you about the last healer. So, no matter how wonderful a healer you are, you will not

get a recommendation from them, and in fact just the opposite. They also tend to be sue happy, so you get these unpleasant lawsuits that can devastate you.

If for some reason you are compelled to work with these types, only work with them on the global trust issue FIRST. But I recommend you avoid them, as their defenses get stimulated by looking at the issue and all hell can break out.

In summary, although you are already great healers in comparison with the people in the field with conventional training, you are still constrained by the limitations of what your clients will do under your instruction. And by the limitations of your experience and training. BE CAUTIOUS! It isn't until you can reach inside someone and heal them directly that some of these restrictions can be loosened, but even here it will be a long time before you are ready for this sort of stuff. And you still need conventional training in the particular issue regardless.

Thanks for letting us sleep better at night.

Key Points:

- Suicidal clients are outside of your level of expertise if you don't have special training and support facilities

- People with heart conditions are at risk for a heart attack during this work, just as they are from any kind of physical stress.

is this a peak ability?

REGENERATIVE HEALING

Healing certain traumas using Whole-Hearted Healing or other techniques sometimes eliminates physical problems, because you release the unconscious efforts that are continuously pushing you from health. However, a variety of conditions, such as late stage terminal cancer, cut spines, damaged teeth, scars, and so on won't respond to these types of methods. Healing these and other serious conditions is possible, but requires a very different approach. We call this approach 'Regenerative Healing' (formerly we called it Radical Physical Healing, but we changed the name to more accurately reflect the nature of the phenomenon). One of the most amazing characteristics of this approach is the speed, as the condition vanishes in front of your eyes in minutes. Like many, I was skeptical of stories of spontaneous or faith healing, until I met a healer who could regularly heal terminal diseases and incurable injuries like AIDS, cancer, or broken backs, typically in a few minutes with no physical intervention.

The secret lies in our past. In the womb, we are actively directing the growth process, not just running some DNA program. Without going into the fascinating details, during birth our body's repair systems go into a sort of autopilot, which we all consider normal. It is possible to bypass this womb experience and 'spontaneously' heal ourselves.

As I mentioned briefly in Day 1, when you heal birth or pre-birth trauma, you're young self is actually doing regenerative healing on its injury(s). By "staying with" the injury at the moment it occurs in these traumas, you eventually come to a resolution with no emotion, no pain, and a feeling of being big and bright inside - *even though the injury producing event is still occurring.* As I've said, with WHH we're actually changing the past - and your prenatal self is healing its body fully in time with what used to cause you harm. An adult example of this was Jack Schwarz, who could run a knitting needle through his arm without damage - he was doing regenerative healing on the fly, just as your prenatal self can. Obviously, being able to do regenerative healing after birth is a fairly rare ability.

A few people actually have the ability to induce this sort of healing into other's bodies, as hard as this is to believe. However, finding the genuine article is pretty unusual, so be an aware consumer. The only person I ever met who could do it consistently, Reverend Dolores Lucas, was able to cure somewhere between 50% and 70% of the people she saw, I'd estimate. Her success rate wasn't a function of the health problem, it was more her resistance to helping. (She no longer does the healing work.) Another individual that can do it on a somewhat regular basis is Harold McCoy of the Ozark Research Institute. Another group that regularly does this is the Chilel Qigong School in China. It turns out that you can improve your odds when you're with this type of healer by trying to recall how it felt to be a fetus, by specifically seeing your body as very large and bright inside, and try and feel a sense of internal wholeness. The key to their method is that apparently they help you feel safe enough so that you heal yourself.

The Institute for the Study of Peak States is currently working on this problem. Fascinating work!

OTHER HEALING TECHNIQUES

Dyslexia

A specific process developed just for dyslexia involves moving the body viewpoint to a particular location either inside or just outside the upper back of the skull, a technique with has dramatic results for dyslexia, as described in *The Gift of Dyslexia* by Ronald Davis.

Past life and other regression techniques

Several good authors do work in this area. Dr. Weiss is a man I've met and liked, so I recommend him on that basis. See his book *Many Lives, Many Masters*. He also gives workshops on mastering regression techniques. For more information on this fascinating work, see *Regression Therapy: A Handbook for Professionals*, Volume 1 and 2 by Winafred Blake Lucas.

However, I have come across a problem with regression techniques in general. Especially with past life material, recalling the trauma is usually enough to give the client a tremendous sense of relief that there is a reason for the problem they are having in their current life. However, I've found that the therapist will often stop at this point, and not help heal the incident in question to eliminate the behavior in the present. This is a vital step, but one of the techniques mentioned above needs to be applied at this point to heal the trauma.

These techniques generally require a trained therapist, but many of them are quick and cost effective, so exploring this area is not too much of a burden. In my experience, however, I found that the techniques used on me were too mild to be effective for me. Thus, the expertise of the therapist, and the tools he's using are probably critical elements in successful work. My WHH technique does bring up this sort of material, but it's not my primary focus—most of a person's day-to-day problems have nothing to do with past lives. I've discovered since then that accessing past lives is due to avoiding a trauma in this life with a similar feel to it. Thus, the core problem will not be removed unless the situation in this life is healed also.

Shamanism and Soul Retrieval for trauma and schizophrenia

Michael Harner has been the dominant force in preserving and promoting ancient shamanic healing techniques in the last 20 years, through his organization The Foundation for Shamanic Studies at 415-380-8282, and with his book *The Way of the Shaman*. His assistant Sandra Ingerman has done a wonderful job of expanding and illustrating one of the primary shamanic techniques in her book *Soul Retrieval* and through trainings worldwide. (http://www.shamanicvisions.com/ingerman.html)

The technique involves healing an aspect of trauma that is not acceptable or understandable in current western world views. Yet, it's very fast, typically 30 minutes or so, and often amazingly effective, and does not involve any effort from the client. Two types of work are the dominant focus; soul loss, which occurs during very serious trauma and causes severe problems to the client; and soul stealing, which results in afflictions like schizophrenia.

I've personally seen dramatic healing of severe mental illness in minutes using these techniques, which are quick and inexpensive. I would recommend that anyone give shamanic healing a try on principle, even if you believe that you don't have any problems. However, it does depend on the abilities of the practitioner, and so the difficulty of knowing if you've gotten a competent one is a problem. This sort of work really can't easily be done on oneself, but training in the techniques is readily available through Harner's organization. I'd guess about 70% of the people attending his workshops have some sort of aptitude for their techniques.

Issues of soul loss and soul stealing come up in WHH. If one is willing, soul stealing can be healed by dealing with certain types of womb and birth experiences, but soul loss is only dealt with on a case by case basis, at least so far, and not all at once as in shamanic work. Too, someone who can't or won't use basic WHH can't be helped, as in cases of severe mental illness, while this is not a problem to the shamanic practitioner.

Hanbleceya Therapeutic Community System for Schizophrenia and other severe mental illnesses

This virtually unknown treatment center in California has the unusual distinction of routinely curing schizophrenia. It usually takes quite a while, sometimes years, and is a live in facility so somewhat costly, but a real bargain if you've got this problem. They also work with bipolar patients and psychosis patients. They primarily use the body therapies of Bio-cellular Integration, which involves breath and movement, bioenergetic analysis, tragering, massage, acupressure, and dance. Call 619-466-0547 for more information. Incidentally, their work is not published in journals because they can never get past peer review—the reviewers cannot believe schizophrenia is curable, so reject the submitted articles. I've had the same sort of problem with my work.

Their cure for schizophrenia goes in two steps. First, the patient comes to realize it's something he is doing to himself. Sometime later, the patient decides to choose not to be schizophrenic. This approach makes perfect sense to me, as they use touch to reassure the body consciousness that it will survive even if it doesn't continue to pull in foreign soul pieces. (See work on healing schizophrenia in *Silencing the Voices: From Mind Chatter to Schizophrenia*.) This is a great way to work with someone that can't or won't do the more direct way of using trauma healing techniques to break the link between survival and outside emotions due to birth and womb trauma. And their technique has the advantage that it doesn't involve any concepts outside of accepted western biases.

However, before pursuing this program, I would start by getting treatment by a competent shamanic practitioner. This might eliminate the problem in a day, which would certainly be cost effective. Or use one of our advanced WHH graduates specializing in healing schizophrenia.

EXERCISE—PRACTICE WHH WITH A PARTNER

This will be the last opportunity to heal issues that we have time for in this workshop. At this point, you've been exposed to everything available at the basic WHH level, and only practice can improve things. I strongly suggest practicing on yourself, as this really drives the lessons home. As you work, you might also be considering if further training in one of the other therapies that have been mentioned in this class would be useful to you.

The training facilitators will be available to you at no charge over the next few weeks to help you if you got stuck on some issue during the workshop. Unfortunately, in the workshop setting it isn't always possible to finish any given issue due to time constraints. Try healing it on your own (you do need the practice, after all), and if you need to, set up a time when you can do a phone session with one of us.

Practice Session Notes:

Practice Session Notes (continued):

ETHICAL ISSUES

At this point, we'd like to just have a brief discussion of ethical issues around the work we're doing. Some points to consider:

- Is it OK to do DPR or surrogate energy therapies on someone without their permission? How about spouses or family members? How about alcoholics or others who won't give permission for you to work on them?

- What is your responsibility to people you use these powerful techniques on, if they open up something like forgotten abuse or birth trauma and then are unable to heal?

- How great does your mastery of WHH or other therapy have to be before you use it to work on friends or clients?

- If you have a client that doesn't heal quickly (or at all), and you are paid by the hour, should you give a refund? Send them to another therapist? Do you offer a guarantee that your work together will be permanent?

- Have you considered working with your client to offer a fixed fee to heal your client's specified problem, and not charging if you don't deliver? With a guarantee?

- What is your responsibility for using EFT (or other energy therapy) if there is a chance it isn't necessarily permanent?   △ NEWSLETTER 13

- Do you need to have training in other power therapies? Go to conferences to keep informed of the latest developments in them or in WHH?

- In this work, we encounter strange phenomena not accepted by our culture (chakras, spiritual emergencies, etc.). Do we ignore them, discount them, try and get more training in them, or what? What do we tell our clients?

CONCLUDING DISCUSSION AND FOLLOW UP RESOURCES

Class evaluation forms

What were the most important things you got from this class? Please remember to fill out the class evaluation forms, so that we can know what to keep, what to change, and what to throw out completely. Remember, you spent 4 days, a lot of pain, and money for the class—was it worth it?

Website practitioner referral list

Too, be sure to put your name and paragraph on our website list of practitioners! Too, if you'd like to volunteer a testimonial for the website, please do so - it's something that we can really use. It's a free service to clients and therapists. One suggestion that Gary Craig, the developer of EFT made with regards to these small self descriptions on the website - clients (and probably you too) want to go to an expert in their particular problem. What is your special area of expertise?

Updates on technique improvements, other therapies, and Institute projects

We try and keep you informed of new information by posting it in the appropriate section of the website www.PeakStates.com. You can also get to the website by going to www.WholeHeartedHealing.com. Be sure to get the email list of your fellow workshop participants - you never know what the future holds! We publish newsletters at infrequent intervals, and you can sign up by going to the website PeakStates.com. We also run an email group for people using the basic WHH technique, and you can be put in the group by signing up on the main page of our site.

Working on Institute projects

Does being a volunteer for advanced work with the Institute interest you? Ask yourself, what burning desire do I have for this lifetime right now? Is that in alignment with the Institute? (For example, playing golf like Tiger Woods, although it might be possible in one of the peak states you could get at the Institute, wouldn't further the aims we have.) You've learned the basic technique we use to investigate a number of areas, such as severe illnesses, regenerative healing, and peak states. You've had a chance to meet us, and find out if we feel compatible. If it feels right, get in touch with us (actually, keep pushing because we sometimes let things slide) to go on to master advanced states of consciousness and become a volunteer with the Institute.

Legal liability and ministerial certification

A brief mention of legal liability when working with clients using basic WHH or in fact any nonstandard therapy is in order. At least in the United States, licenses are generally required to do psychotherapy, although the particulars vary from state to state. However, if you use any non-standard therapies, such as virtually any power therapy, you can be sued. Although this situation is improving, liability is a concern. And in fact, being sued is probably a risk no matter what you do. One way to not get involved with this catch-22 situation is to get become a church minister and practice under their auspices. Although any denomination would work, may I suggest using the Association for the Whole Person (AIWP). They do exceptional work, and becoming ordained is not too difficult. They are based out of Ronert Park, California, and their phone number is 707-586-9484. Their email is aiwp@aol.com.

Another religious organization that grants a ministerial license is the Universal Life Church at www.ulc.org. It is worldwide, and may be able to help with clergy insurance.

Another organization can be found at http://spirtualhumanism.org - this one has no requirement to study or agree to doctrine, or to pay any money to be ordained as a minister.

What this course did not cover

In the basic WHH course, we've tried to restrict the material to what an average person in an average state of consciousness could master. This is adequate for most therapists. Advanced WHH focuses on learning what causes peak states of consciousness, how to acquire them, and how to use them. It's also designed to teach you how to heal people at a distance, and how to heal certain types of illnesses like schizophrenia. Occasionally this level of work is needed in order to help your client (or yourself), but it generally doesn't come up in a normal therapy situation. Learning the advanced material also allows you to help us do more research and development for the Institute.

Teaching basic Whole-Hearted Healing

Like EFT, we're happy when people teach the basic WHH process to clients or the public. Feel free to download and reproduce for your workshops the teaching materials off of our website www.PeakStates.com to help you do so, and ask questions or get help from us. The materials are free, although copyrighted. Of course, we expect ethical behavior, which among other things means that you've done the process enough to have mastered it adequately. Good luck!

However, to teach through our Institute we presently require that you've learned the advanced techniques. This is because of two factors: 1) We're primarily teaching this material in order to meet new people who wish to join in on our work. Our scheduled workshops give folks a chance to meet the rest of us, in order to find out if they want to get involved; and 2) by mastering the more advanced material, the teachers understand what the basic lessons are preparing the students for. It's just like learning and teaching algebra after you've learned calculus - you have a feel for what the limitations of algebra are and what you really need to understand in order to move to the next level.

After the workshop:

If unhealed material is brought up in class but isn't healed, please work on it yourself or contact one of the instructors for help. Since our time in the workshop was so limited, we don't expect that you will have finished all of your issues. Please write down in your manual our phone numbers - we'll be checking them regularly over the next few days just in case.

PEAK STATES OF CONSCIOUSNESS:
TRAUMA RELIEF USING THE INNER PEACE PROCESS (IPP)

In Appendix G is a handout describing the Inner Peace Process. Although we retain the copyright, we've included it in this manual so that you can photocopy it and hand it out to clients and students who want to try the process. Only one restriction—we want you to hand out all of it, as it gives clients a clear idea of the pro's and con's of the process.

Turn to the appendix now and read the first section about peak states of consciousness. If you want more information about peak states of consciousness, we refer you to our *Peak States of Consciousness*: Volumes 1 to 3.

The IPP was developed because we needed a simple way to put people into peak states. We'd found that we could do so by regressing to certain developmental events before birth, but this was not practical for most therapists and clients to do. Instead, we use the energy therapy EFT, a phrase, and music to do the same thing. As I've said numerous times, the drawback to meridian therapies is that they can potentially be undone by accident. However, in this case we didn't consider it a drawback as it made the process easy and fast. If it came undone, a client could just do it again.

The IPP puts about half of the client population into a peak state of consciousness, the Inner Peace state. In this state, the client experiences a sense of peace under whatever else they're feeling. This occurs because the state puts them in the present moment in time. Although this is worthwhile by itself, as therapists there is a much more valuable feature to the state - it makes all past emotional trauma *stop feeling traumatic*. As you might imagine, this is incredibly important to our clients. WHH starts by asking the client if they feel calm, peace, and lightness about an issue. In the Inner Peace state, they not only feel an underlying calm, past emotional material just doesn't come through into the present. This has tremendous impact on people's behavior, although interestingly most people don't notice the state after a few days - they get used to the fact that their 'triggers' are missing and old emotional issues just don't arise anymore.

We're particularly interested in what else this state does for people. I hope that you will keep us informed of any unusual changes that occur in yourself or your clients.

> **Example:** A woman who went into the Inner Peace state using the IPP had addictions to alcohol and drugs. After the process, testing showed her past emotional traumas were at a 0 SUDS rating. Months later, she reported that she was still struggling with addictions, and had mostly lost the state. However, her suicidal feelings had completely vanished and never returned, even though she didn't have the full Inner Peace state.

Now turn back to Appendix G and read the section 'The Inner Peace Process' and 'The Inner Peace Process Steps'.

Over the next few years, we expect we'll improve the process. For example, you might want to try and incorporate TAT into the process to see if it works better for your clients.

We also have a two hour video of a workshop where we did the Inner Peace Process. The first half hour covers the material in the IPP handout, and the rest is the actual process being done. People watching the tape can do the process as they watch, as if it were an exercise video. It can be purchased via our website at www.PeakStates.com.

Questions and Answers

1. If you or your client already has a peak state, is there any value in doing this process?

Answer: Yes. States can be accumulated like marbles, and if they don't already have a state characterized by peace and a lack of emotionally traumatic past incidents, they should definitely add this one! Secondly, even if they have this state, The process can stabilize the state. By stabilize I mean they become less prone to ever falling out of the state. Third, triune brain states build upon each other. We've had people in our workshops who already felt great, with wonderful peak states, have dramatic new states appear because this one was the one they were missing, and the better ones suddenly appeared once this piece was in place.

EXERCISE—DO THE INNER PEACE PROCESS

Familiarize yourself with the process described in the previous section. Be sure to ask any questions that occur to you, as your clients will be sure to ask the same ones. Note the questions that your classmates have. We'll be working in pairs again, with one person being the therapist and the other being the client. Start by filling out Appendix K to evaluate your state of consciousness. We're going to have you fill out the form after the process too, to be used as research for the Institute. We've included a duplicate form so you can keep a copy for yourself, if you wish.

Try experimenting—does it feel better if you, as the client, repeats the phrase too, remains silent, or mixes the two? Is it better if you tap yourself, or is it better if the therapist taps you? Notice that just repeating the phrase without doing the EFT doesn't change anything. What do you do if nothing appears to be happening? Did you remember to note down traumatic issues to use as a test for the state?

As we discovered, change continues to happen long after the SUDS levels go to zero. Keep taping on your client. Give yourself at least 30 minutes, and preferable 60 minutes to work with the phrase. Note what happens that you didn't expect.

Practice Session Notes:

Practice Session Notes (continued):

THE HOLLOW/BRIGHTNESS PEAK STATE INDUCTION PROCESS

(Note to instructors: The following part of the class is generally done on a fifth day of the training, as it takes considerable time. Contact us for the latest Gaia instructions.)

A description of the Hollow/Brightness state

This process is designed to put participants into the Hollow and Inner Brightness states, where the brains are all fused, and there is an experience of bright internal light. In this combination state, you will feel hollow inside, as if your body inside your skin turned into air, like you'd become an empty tin can. When you cover your eyes, you experience a bright clear light in your head (or a bright black fluorescent light when it's combined with another peak state that's beyond the scope of this class).

Why would you want to be in this combination state? This state is one that is most useful for our work in the Institute, as well as making healing using WHH virtually pain free. You'll find that life seems pretty effortless, and you're calm and peaceful no matter what happens in your life. It also gives a host of unusual abilities that you may or may not discover on your own. Additionally, with this state you can easily acquire other major peak states once you're shown how. One of the reason's we usually put the peak state processes at the end of the workshop is that if the process works, you'll feel so good that you won't have any issues that you can find to practice WHH on!

About the process:

Since the process is not yet finished and is still very experimental, we require that you do not use it on your clients if you haven't had further training. You don't yet have the knowledge to handle any unusual problems that come up. Also, we don't want an incomplete and not thoroughly tested procedure to be passed out to the public. There may be some unexpected side effects that only certain people have that might be dangerous, harmful, or painful. After all, what are you going to do if there are unexpected side effects and someone outside of class gets into trouble? Too, we don't want people to try a procedure that isn't fully effective, have nothing happen, and decide the whole thing is untrue.

The Hollow/Brightness process is very similar to the Inner Peace process. Review the Inner Peace process for the basic steps and instructions. Unlike that process, this one involves many more phrases. If you think of the Perry diagram, what we're trying to have you do is bring all your awarenesses together into one ball. Since we haven't finished deriving all the steps needed, what you can expect is that you'll only get partway to that goal. At some point in the process you will stop changing and will be at one of the states on the way to completely fusing all the brains together. Although you might feel disappointed if you don't make it all the way, any of the fusion substates is a lot better than average consciousness!

The procedure is designed to be done one phrase at a time. People's speed in working through these feelings varies drastically, so don't be concerned if it's 'taking too long'. We'll be providing a CD and a list of phrases for you to work with, and if you wish you could repeat the process at home for a longer duration to be sure you got out of it as much as possible. Notice that you might find that you enter the hollow state in only one area of your body at a time, for example your head or arm became like air but the rest of you was still flesh. This means that you need to keep tapping on the current phrase until the changes go to completion.

We've also discovered that some people need to heal whatever major 'stuff' has their attention in the present before the process takes affect. These are usually life long, major issues that block the process from working. Interestingly, you can do the process, heal the issue later, and as you complete it, you'll just pop into a relatively permanent peak state.

We expect around 25% of the course participants will enter the Hollow/Brightness state, at least temporarily. Another 50% should be in the Inner Peace substate or better, and we expect about 25% to have no reaction. And generally, the process appears to be relatively permanent - you may leave the state from time to time after the process, but will soon return to it or a slightly lesser state - at least, that's our experience so far. Thus, if you decide to use the procedure, be aware that it's pretty much a one-way street - once you've gone into the state, chances are really good that you're not going to be able to get rid of it.

The exact phrases and music are handed out in class, as this process is continuously changing as we continue to improve it. See *Peak States of Consciousness: Volume 2* for a complete theoretical derivation of the process.

Possible states you might end up with

You may not get to the target state, but rather one of the lesser ones in the list below. Approximately, a person builds up to the brilliance state from the lesser states listed. If something happens that doesn't allow you to get one of them, you can't go any further. This is because this process is focusing on states where your body, heart and mind become one. If you imagine that each of these parts of yourself is self aware, you can imagine that the individual self awarenesses are like spheres of light lined up vertically in your body (where the head, heart, and belly are located). What we're trying to do is make the spheres coalesce into one big ball of light, located around your lower diaphragm. Since we haven't finished deriving all the steps needed, what you can expect is that you'll only get partway to that goal, unless you were lucky enough that you didn't need the step that's missing. You might get the head and heart spheres together, or not quite, or almost on all three, and so on. At some point in the process you will stop changing and will be at one of the states on the way to completely fusing all the brains together. Although you might feel disappointed if you don't make it all the way, any of the fusion or merged substates is a lot better than average consciousness!

To make this clearer, we'll draw 'Perry diagrams' in the class to explain the different types of brain states. It's drawn as a vertical row of circles whose overlap and distance from each other indicate the degree of fusion of awarenesses among the brains.

In the section on the Inner Peace Process was a very brief description of several of these brain fusion states. You might want to refer to these descriptions as you go through the induction process, to try and see if you've gotten the listed state.

There are quite a number of peak states that that don't have anything to do with brain fusion states. The process you're using today is not designed to give you any of them except by accident. They're worked with in the advanced Whole-Hearted Healing training. If you're curious, you can check the Peak States website for brief descriptions of these other types of states.

Changes you might find disturbing:

One of the most frequently asked questions is what problems you might have with these states. Often participants don't realize that what they now experience is a sign of health because they've never felt it before. Specifically,

• The sensation of no longer having flesh inside your skin can be disturbing intellectually, although it feels fine.

• When your body feels like it's become air, often you will become aware that the shell layer at your skin feels uncomfortable, like it burns a bit.

• Some complain that the brightness in their head and body makes it difficult to sleep, as if they were trying to sleep outside in the sunshine with their eyes open. This reaction is due to trauma, and can be eliminated quite easily. Often it's due to the bright light being painful when they were born.

- Although we're targeting the Hollow/Brightness state, occasionally you'll get other states too. Since you were not expecting them, you might be concerned. Some that might occur: your body suddenly feels drastically sacred; your skin feels like it vanished also and your awareness spreads through space; you find you can 'see' into the flesh of your body; etc.

- Vision might change. Everything might suddenly look three dimensional in comparison to what you're used to; you can see behind objects, or through them or your eyelids, etc.

- Emotions feel quite different. They're more like having thoughts, not feelings. For someone who has had and likes vivid feelings, this can feel peculiar, although it is comfortable.

- If you are in a life crisis, you won't react and it may feel odd to have your world crumbling around you and still feel quite fine.

- You might go into a lesser peak fusion state, such as having your 'brains touching' state. Now, when you go to do things, you'll find that each of the brains may have an opinion, and can communicate it directly to your awareness. It's a bit startling, like having a bunch of kids you never paid attention to start 'talking'.

Specific procedure

We start by filling out the state evaluation form at the end of this document. This is for research purposes for the Institute. There are 5 blank columns so that we can have you fill out the form each time you experience something unusual occurring in your state or awareness. Be sure to write down what that change was, as well as filling out the column.

Be sure to ask any questions that occur to you! You will work in pairs, with one person guiding (the 'therapist') and one person receiving (the 'client') the process, then switching. There is a list of phrases with accompanying music, body postures, and visualizations below. The same procedure is repeated for every phrase.

The process starts with at least one minute of TAT. You might want to experiment, but what we've been doing is have them go into the TAT pose while both the client and the therapist keep repeating the phrase over and over while the music is playing. If the client finds it too distracting, they can stop saying the phrase. After the TAT, we then use EFT. The therapist repeats the phrase over and over while he does EFT tapping on each meridian point. The phrase is repeated at each tapping point. Generally the client repeats it at the same time, although again some clients find saying it too distracting. Don't change the wording, it needs to be done as stated. We've found that just doing the tapping points followed by doing a psychological reversal step at the end of each round on whatever the client is feeling at the moment is generally sufficient. The psychological reversal step is done by tapping the karate point (or rubbing the chest if the karate point doesn't appear to be working) while they use the standard phrase, "Even though I feel ... I deeply and completely accept myself." Then the tapping sequence is repeated, again saying the phrase at every meridian point. Tapping on the client is generally more successful, although there is no problem with having them tap themselves if they're getting results. The Nine Gamut procedure is not used.

Visualize with eyes closed is optimum. Sequencing of phrases is irrelevant.

The process won't work if you successfully ignore any symptoms that arise. Note that a number of people try and explain the arising sensations as due to what's going on in the classroom currently. Although a natural reaction, trying to do this might block the process. Either you may not see the need to tap out these symptoms also, since they feel that it's appropriate for what's going on, or you won't focus on them because you don't see them as relevant.

Try experimenting—does it feel better if you as the client repeats the phrase too, remains silent, or mixes the two? Is it better if you tap yourself, or is it better if the therapist taps you? Notice that just repeating the phrase without doing the EFT doesn't change anything. What do you do if nothing appears to be happening? Did you remember to note down traumatic issues to use as a test for the state?

The procedure is designed to be done one phrase at a time. Swap the roles between therapist and client for each message, so that you keep in step. People's speed in working through the feelings that arise varies drastically, so don't be concerned if it's 'taking too long'. We'll be providing a CD and a list of phrases for you to work with, and if you wish you can repeat the process at home for a longer duration to be sure you got out of it as much as possible.

Notice that you might find that you enter the hollow state in only one area of your body at a time, for example your head or arm became like air but the rest of you was still flesh. This means that you need to keep tapping on the current phrase until the changes go to completion.

You continue the pattern for a couple of rounds past any additional changes. This instruction can be quite tricky, as the client has had the traumatic feeling for their entire life, so they consider the sensations to be normal. Thus they don't realize that they do have symptoms that they need to continue tapping on. This part of the procedure usually takes around 5 to 15 minutes. To our surprise, we've found that if you continue the process for a long time, for most people change continues to happen. Several hours of tapping spread over a couple of sessions is often required to get the full change that can happen. Continuing in this way also makes the client less likely to fall out of the state.

We've also discovered that some people need to heal whatever major 'stuff' has their attention in the present before the process takes affect. These are usually life long, major issues that block the process from working. Interestingly, you can do the process, heal the issue later, and as you complete it, you'll just pop into a relatively permanent peak state.

Question and answers

1. From "Head to Heart" to "Brilliance" - are these states successively passed through, or do you aim for one, any one in a session, or do you go further up the ladder the more often you practice the peak state process?

    Answer: At this time, we think that some people's state will be improved by more practice, because some subtle material was missed the first times. The Join forces in Glory' phrase is a good example of this for a lot of people. If you tapped on a phrase just enough to squeak by on a good day, more tapping would lock it in better. Since EFT is potentially reversible, repeating the sequence would reverse the reversal. The states are not necessarily passed through, as it depends on the sequencing of how the three brains merge together.

2. Do you go through all consecutively or only some (see question 1)?

    Answer: To the participant, it may feel like they skip some states, as they had the corresponding developmental moments already healed, and so skip to a better state once the more basic blocks were out of the way.

3. I don't know or even have most of the music, but even if I did, would I keep tapping during the whole song, more than three rounds or stop the music thus interrupting the process and put on the next song, or...

    Answer: Put the music on repeat, and keep tapping. Interrupting might cause you to need another round to get back into the trauma moment the phrase is accessing.

4. How do I do the "body", for example: Left hand / arm across front, right across back, both horizontally, while tapping or holding the TAT pose?

   Answer: Do the best you can. The process is really designed to be done with a partner who does the TAT and EFT on you.

Exercise—Do the Hollow/Brightness Peak State Induction Process

We'll be handing out the steps in class, along with an appropriate music CD. Please stop whenever you experience a significant change, note what step you were on, and fill out the questions on the peak state evaluation form along with what happened. (Appendix K). Good luck!

Practice Session Notes:

Practice Session Notes (continued):

Appendixes

APPENDIX A—SAMPLE CLIENT LETTER & INTAKE FORM

Your Name

Your Business Name

Your phone number

Welcome

This is a reminder of how you should prepare, what you should do and can expect after a session in the office using the new generation of therapeutic techniques called 'Power Therapies'.

How to prepare for a session

Please come in with an idea of the issue you wish to heal. This saves us time (and you money).

Please do not schedule any activity immediately after your session, as we may run over the standard hour. Unlike regular therapists, we continue to do healing with you until we are at a good stopping place. Since the client before you is in the same situation, occasionally we might be delayed in getting to your treatment. Thanks for your understanding.

Occasionally after a session, you'll be very tired. This is normal, so just treat yourself gently and don't schedule activity that you cannot miss after our work.

What we will do during the session

We may use a technique that involves gentle tapping on acupressure points. You will remain fully clothed, and with some practice can do it for yourself. The treatment is generally very rapid, and you will not generally spend much time discussing your issue or feeling or expressing your emotions around it.

During the session, you may experience emotional or physical pain from events in your past, even events that you have forgotten, that are causing you difficulties in the present. They usually dissolve quickly as we work.

In the session I will give you a record of the issue we worked on, how badly you felt about it, and what memories if any came up. With these new types of therapy, you more often than not forget that the issue was ever painful to you, or sometimes that you even had the issue at all! Since we want you to continue healing, a written record gives you something to remind yourself that what we did made a difference.

What to do after a session

Immediately after a session, I strongly recommend that you write down what you experienced, and any insights that you might have. If you wait even a day, you will find that the issue is very hard to recall. This can be useful for your healing.

Please check back with me in 2 or 3 days to let me go how the issue feels, and what else might be up for you now. It is important to me to make sure that your healing is supported even after you leave the office.

If any emotional or physical difficulty should arise in the next 24 hours, please call me immediately. This almost never happens, but if it should, don't hesitate to call day or night. My office phone is 000-000, and my home number is 000-0000.

Forgetting you had a problem

After a successful session, you will probably find in the few days that it's difficult to believe that you ever had an issue. This is a common result of healing, because there isn't any residual feeling left. Similarly, it's difficult to believe that the work you did in the office was responsible for the problem disappearing. Unfortunately, these common reactions to healing may keep you from getting help on other issues. To guard against this, we strongly recommend you write down before you come to therapy how you feel about your issue so that later, you can read what you've written to help you remember that what we did today made a difference in your life.

Self Study

For self study, we recommend the following:

- Emotional Freedom Technique (EFT)—a free manual can be downloaded from www.emofree.com; this web site also has a huge resource of tips and case studies for review or you can order a self study video course for about $180US, or download the manual for free.

- Tapas Acupressure Technique (TAT)—Workshops and manuals are available. Contact www.tat-intl.com

- Whole-Hearted Healing (WHH)—A free study guide is at the website www.PeakStates.com, and training is available.

We are happy that we could serve you.

Sincerely,

Your Name

Client intake information

Name _____   **Date** _____

Address
_____

Phone (work) _____   **Phone (home)** _____

Email address
(print carefully)
_____

How did you learn about us:

Contact in case of emergencies:

Name and phone number of primary care physician:

Any potentially life threatening conditions, like heart trouble or breathing problems:

Problem client wishes resolved. Rating of severity (0 -10 scale):

Any generational aspects to the problem (relatives, ancestors, siblings):

Allergies or other physical sensitivities that might affect treatment:

Current physical problems:

Current psychoactive medications:

For the therapist, after a session:

1.   Issue:

2.   SUDS rating:

3.   Outcome:

4.   What worked:

5.   What didn't:

APPENDIX B—STEPS FOR BASIC WHOLE-HEARTED HEALING™

Basic Whole-Hearted Healing™ Step by Step Guide

Revision 4.1 © Grant McFetridge 2000

Step 1. Pick something that's bothering you in the present. Write it down, and note how badly it makes you feel.

Step 2. Briefly focus on feeling in your body the feeling this situation brings up.

Step 3. Recall incidents when you felt exactly like this (often the situations are quite different). Choose the earliest one that has a clear image. Jot down the memories you skipped over. Use the 'loving yourself' technique to help access memories if needed.

Step 4. Place your hand on your chest to remind you to stay in your body in the past.

Step 5. Move into your body in the image, and merge your past and present self. If this is difficult, try simultaneously: a) loving yourself, b) white light, c) relax diaphragm, throat, jaw, d) hyperventilate before or during, e) cranial hold, f) diaphragm massage, g) position at time of trauma, h) rhythmic wavelike motion. See text for details.

Step 6. Iterate on the following steps, separately or all together. Continue until only peace is left, or an earlier memory arises:

1. Recall the phrase (belief, decision) you thought that matches the body sensation at that moment (2-6 words).

2. Feel the body sensations, including any physical pain.

3. Feel the emotion while staying in your chest in the past. Stay with this until the emotion ends. If another emotion arises, stay with it until it ends to be sure it also ends, and no more arise.

4. Stay in the trauma at least 3 minutes after the last change occurs.

Step 7. If an earlier memory image appeared, move to that moment and repeat step 6. Continue to earlier and earlier memories until no more arise. Use the 'loving yourself' technique to access earlier memories. The earliest memory always involves damage to the body, and there may be several damage memories in a series.

Step 8. Check your work. The out of body image should be gone, with only an in-body image. If you flash to the memory, there should be no twinge of pain. Memories that you skipped over should no longer have any feeling to them. In womb, body should feel large and bright.

Step 9. Return to the present. You should no longer feel anything at all about the current situation except calm, peace, and lightness. If some new feeling about the situation has arisen, repeat the entire process over and over until nothing is left.

Special Situations

Emptiness

Feel around your body looking for the origin of the sensation of emptiness and lack. Move your awareness into the emptiness, and or press on the spot, looking for an image of when you were physically hurt in that location.

Holes

If you see a bottomless black pit in your body that feels like a deficient emptiness, move your attention into the hole, and wait until an image arises of when you were physically injured in that area. Is a more dramatic version of 'emptiness' above.

"New" Physical Pain

Rarely, physical pain arises seemingly from nowhere while healing. An earlier memory has surfaced only enough for the pain to be felt. Use direct touch and loving yourself to access the memory more clearly, then heal it.

Womb Memories

Every womb memory has a physical injury associated with it. Stay with it until the pain is gone. The fetal self returns to full brightness once severe injury is healed.

Birth Memories

Focus on the area of physical pain and injury that has come up. Use the holding breath technique briefly if you are resisting the panic (see text).

Copies

If it feels like the feeling is in your body has the tone of someone else (i.e. mother, father, etc.), recall what you yourself felt at that moment to release the copy. Later, go back and eliminate the desire to moving into another's heart region to copy their emotional material. Often a problem with adult healers, therapists, etc.

Self Images and Identities

Look for the feeling associated with them, and track them back to the trauma source. Exaggerating any characteristic physical pose or movements helps focus and recall.

Positive Emotional Memories

Positive emotions associated with a memory need to be healed also, and usually conceal some painful emotional content.

Depression:

Look for a phrase that you are trying not to think. After the phrase is found and the depression vanishes, look for any contributing traumas.

Past Lives

Heal in the same way as in this life. Don't go into judgment, or try and change the past (at least until you don't need to anymore). If you died in a past life, stay with your body until all life is gone and you are at peace. After healing the past life, heal the similar trauma in this life that caused you to access the past life trauma.

"Soul" Stealing

If what appears to be a cloud of smoke, or images of people leave your body while healing a trauma, note the triggering feeling. Later, go back into birth and womb trauma and heal the conviction that your survival depends on having the triggering emotion surround you. See text on mental illness, possession, channeling, and shamanism.

"Soul" Loss

Rarely, after healing a trauma a sensation of loss and lack is left centered in the chest. Missing 'soul' piece will eventually return without intervention, but can bring it back in minutes by singing out loud the piece of music that first comes to mind. Will be a 'pop' sensation at return, and lack will vanish.

Internal Archetypal Images

If you feel a powerful archetypal or demigod image with overwhelming impact inside yourself, (ex. the monster in the basement, the goddess Diana, an Aztec god that rips out hearts), search for the trauma, usually birth, that fits the feeling of this projection and heal it.

Structures in your body

Occasionally, while healing you will suddenly 'see' or feel structures in your body, such as rods connecting places together, or containers enclosing areas. Stay in that moment in the past until they dissolve also.

Chakras

Chakra energy bouncing back from the skin boundary can cause considerable pain. Look for the trigger that causes the chakra to operate, something your mother did while you were *in utero*. (Resisted crown chakra energy feels like pressure pushing down, with each point of pressure having a trauma associated with it.)

Aliveness, Wholeness, Sacred, No self

You may move into these states after certain traumas are healed. Look for trigger or cue to bring you back to these states.

Medication

A few psychologically active medications block this process (ex. desipramine, zanex, klonopin).

APPENDIX C—STEPS FOR DISTANT PERSONALITY RELEASE

Step 1: Relax and focus on the person you want to heal. Get a sense of their presence. They do not have to be physically present for this to work. If you want to heal a particular personality issue that you feel about the person, focus on that, but in general in couples work just focus on whatever it is that bothers you about the person. You will get a sense of them, in exactly the same way you have all your life with other people. Nothing new here, or complicated. Examples would be the client's sadness, suicidal feelings, hatred of you, uncertainty, secretiveness, etc. Incidentally, if you can sense anything about the client, whether it is positive or negative, it is a problem for them. Especially in the case of a 'nice' personality, this can be difficult to believe, but this is because the personality level you're feeling is a shell or defense that the person has constructed around themselves due to trauma.

Step 2: Love the client _for_ having the problem. Rather than loving them in spite of the problem, which is what we normally do, feel it is the problem that is actually what makes them lovable. For example, if the person is a smoker, feel that it is their smoking, which makes them lovable. To emphasize this, I'm asking you to see them as lovable because they have the problem, and in fact they would be less lovable if they didn't have it! Use EFT or WHH or temporarily put aside any of your negative feelings about the characteristic or feeling you are trying to heal in them. This is a critical step for two reasons. If you do not, you cannot help the person let the problem go, and in fact you get into a power struggle with them as you try and force them to let something go. Secondly, this helps you eliminate the tendency in your own life to attract this particular problem in people to yourself. This is the step that people have the most difficulty with. If the process isn't working, this is the step that has gone wrong every time so far in my experience. (If you use EFT or another power therapy to get to peace about how you feel about their feeling, you still can feel their feeling even though you now feel perfectly calm, peaceful and lightness about it. This demonstrates that what you feel in another person isn't just a projection of your own personal material.)

Another way to get the correct feeling of loving someone for their problem is to recall someone who you loved no matter what, like a small child you loved even if they were having a temper tantrum, get the loving feeling going, and bring the image of the child (for example) into the person you are working on. Seeing how they are as the response to old trauma, and feeling the love you had for the child superimposed on the current person seems to do the trick for some people.

Step 3: This next part is actually the part that eliminates the energetic connection. **Now, admire this incredible being for their amazing ability to hang onto the problem no matter what.** Realize how awesome they are for being able to do this no matter what's going on in their lives. Focus your admiration and love on them and how wonderful they are for being able to have held onto the problem so well. A step that can aid this is to imagine that the problem they have is like a cloud around them. (In some cases, it may feel like a shell layer to you.) And it's connected to them by some sort of chords, energy bands, rainbows, octopus tentacles, or whatever you sense at this point. Interestingly, this is what people actually report without prompting when you have them 'look' at the issue the person has. This sensing is useful to give you a feeling of the being who is actually under the cloud, but it isn't actually necessary to be able to actually perceive this level of phenomena. The process works anyway, regardless of your 'psychic' sensing ability. Incidentally, when working on oneself, you can direct love at the connections, causing the connections to break apart.

Step 4: Keep your admiration going for a minute or so, or until you feel a change in them. I'm not sure which way is better, although generally I just have students end after a minute. Now, pull yourself back into your room, look around, focus on your surroundings. Then focus on the client again. Amazingly, the client will feel different. If they don't, make sure step 2 is actually done correctly. Apparently, our admiration at this level is enough to cause the person to relax and let the problem go. This can feel quite dramatic depending on what you're working on. For example, one client felt hatred, and then the next layer down was confusion. It's this experience which really strikes home the fact that you are actually working on someone else's psyche. Not only do they suddenly feel different, but often in ways that you would never anticipate. We have the belief that when we think about a person and feel their presence, it is a projection of our feelings about them, but this turns out to be untrue in general. We are actually experiencing them in real time. This will become obvious to you as the client changes while you watch and experience them.

Step 5: They should now feel different to you. If they don't feel peaceful or vanish from your mental view, the next layer in the onion has surfaced and also needs to be healed. Repeat the process (steps 2 through 4) for this new feeling. Keep this going until all you can feel as the next layer is a sense of peace, or until they have completely vanished from your perception. In my own case, I found that the initial problem would return in time if we didn't continue the process down to the end point of peace, although I've had other clients who stayed changed even if we didn't eliminate all the layers. The reason they may just suddenly vanish from your perception is because they have suddenly (and temporarily) released their entire personality defense structure.

Alternative method for Step 2—Expanded DPR:

We found that sometimes jumping right into step 2 (Loving the person for having the issue, trait, etc.) was a bit daunting. This progressive process gives you a "running start" for getting into a place where you can do the standard DPR steps.

Step 2A: State what you found in Step 1 of DPR in a way that fits what you sense.

Now just sit with that statement until you can accept it as true. This might be very easy or difficult. Listen to the internal dialog you are having about the issue as you work on accepting this. When the internal dialog is quiet and every part of you is in agreement with the statement go to the next step.

Step 2B: Take your statement of "What is" and restate it with "It's okay that..." in front. Often there will be an internal problem with that and the internal dialog goes on around and around until all the "participants" to this dialog can agree that: "It's okay that...whatever you're statement is." When everyone is on board with this step go on to the next step.

Step 2C: Now take the statement and restate it this time putting "I accept that..." in front. Again notice the dialog and continue till all agree with this. Then go on to step 3 of standard DPR.

APPENDIX D—SUMMARY PROCEDURE FOR EFT

THE SETUP: Repeat 3 times…this affirmation:

"Even though I **have** this……?   (or Even though I **still have** some of this……?)
I deeply and completely accept myself."

> While continuously rubbing the Sore Spot,
> Or tapping the karate chop point.

THE SEQUENCE: Tap about <u>7 times</u> on each of the following energy points while repeating the Reminder Phrase at each point.

EB = Beginning of the eyebrow
SE = Side of the Eye
UE = Under the Eye
UN = Under the Nose
Ch = Chin

CB = Beginning of the collarbone

UA = Under the Arm
Th = Thumb
IF = Index Finger
MF = Middle Finger
BF = Baby Finger
KC = Karate Chop

FIRST   THIRD   FIFTH   SEVENTH

SECOND   FOURTH   SIXTH   EIGHTH

The 9 Gamut Procedure:
Continuously tap on the Gamut point while performing each of these 9 actions:

1. **Eyes closed**   2. **Eyes open**   3. **Eyes hard down right**
4. **Eyes hard down left**   5. **Roll eyes in circle**   6. **Roll eyes in the other direction**
7. **Hum 2 seconds of a song** 8. **Count to 5**   9. **Hum 2 seconds of a song**

THE SEQUENCE (again):   Tap about <u>7 times</u> on each of the following energy points while repeating the Reminder Phrase at each point.
EB, SE, UE, UN, Ch, CB, UA, Th, IF, MF, BF, KC

NOTE: In each subsequent round, the **Setup Affirmation** and the **Reminder Phrase** is adjusted to reflect that you are addressing the **<u>remaining</u>** problem.

From Gary Craig (www.emofree.com)

APPENDIX E—PROCEDURE FOR UNDOING / REVERSING EFT

February 20, 2000

Introduction

Below is a method that our tests showed would often reverse (undo) the healing that EFT gives. I feel this is important for you to know, since: 1) This knowledge allows us to either warn our clients to avoid doing it; or 2) to cause us as practitioners to emphasize that if a problem returns, to just tap it out again, or 3) choose an non meridian based therapy for the clients problem if the issue is one that would be difficult to easily heal again with EFT. A method that minimizes this problem is also below.

Preliminary steps for Undoing EFT

These are the steps we've identified so far. Not every step is required to undo every trauma, issue, or condition.

1. Focus on the problem feeling, just as if doing normal EFT

2. Tense the diaphragm and throat. One way this can be done is to breath in a way that is the opposite of normal breathing, i.e., suck up the diaphragm on an in breath while tensing the throat.

3. Initiate a sort of shuddery sensation, as if one were cold, with the kinesthetic feeling of pulling into oneself, as if pulling a blanket tight over one's body. This last step is not necessary in many cases.

> **Example:** A client inadvertently reversed healing we'd done with EFT. She had an issue involving the feeling of dying. After successful treatment, involving a womb trauma, her experience of everyday life radically improved. Eight days later, after a kayaking trip, her improved condition reversed itself. What happened was as follows: she was kayaking, and it looked like they would all be killed in bad weather on the ocean. She was feeling that she might die (Step 1). She was frantically paddling, straining and breathing hard as she fought the waves (Step 2). And she was cold after hours in the water (step 3). The reversal of healing was dramatically noted after that by the client.

The Initial Experiment

In this test, we deliberately asked for volunteers who knew EFT to try and reverse the healing effects of EFT. Since we didn't know what might be the key pieces in reversal, we had the participants focus on two types of traumas from their pasts, and experiment on themselves. The first trauma type was purely emotional, while the second had a physical injury associated with the emotional content. We had the participants tap out the first trauma, then try to undo it in any way they could think of. We repeated the process for the second physical trauma, and again asked participants to try and undo it. We iterated when one person discovered that moving his diaphragm opposite to normal breathing was effective in undoing the tapping. Below is a tabulation of how many people could undo the trauma and how many couldn't. Essentially, they were just using Step 2 by itself.

	Undone	Unchanged	Other
Emotional Trauma	2	7	0
Physical Trauma	4	4	1

(The 'other' case was fascinating, and gives a different verification of this test. The person could undo the trauma while using the reversing breath, but it would go back to peace as soon as she stopped the breath reversal.)

From this experiment we isolated what seemed to be the key pieces for undoing EFT, noted above as three steps.

Comments

Apparently, meridian therapies act to sort of soothe or relax the body, causing it to stop triggering stored emotional and physical material from past traumas. However, after an EFT treatment the stored trauma is still in storage, just not available. Thus, EFT is like using whiteout on a catalog entry (the trauma trigger) in the library, while leaving the volume (the traumatic emotional and physical content) in the stacks.

In Step 2 above, tensing the throat and diaphragm acts to reinforce separation between the body (reptilian brain), heart (mammalian brain), and mind (primate brain). Tensing the diaphragm is a key piece in storing traumatic material. For more information, refer to our *Peak States of Consciousness, Volume 1.*

Step 3 above, involving a shuddery pulling towards oneself, is particularly interesting. This action tightens a layer around the body, which contains some allergy response, information and other 'inherited' problems. Hence, the shuddery tightening feeling apparently makes the information content in the layer become more dominant, and induces the observed phenomena of 'energy toxins'. At our Institute, we call this surface layer the shell, or ego/personality, and it is what gives us the sensation of having a boundary at our skin. For more on this, see www.PeakStates.com.

Recommendations

- Continue to use EFT and it's cousins mostly as we always have, because under most circumstances they are still fast, simple, and effective therapies. Their use is an incredible boon to suffering clients, and is radically changing the expectations of clients, therapists, and performance coaches worldwide.

- Take good notes during a session so that for difficult cases the client can quickly get back to the core issue of the presenting problem if the EFT becomes undone.

- For severe trauma which would be difficult for the client to face or access by themselves, such as birth or womb injury, I would recommend using a non-meridian based power therapy, such as WHH (Whole-Hearted Healing) or TIR (Traumatic Incident Reduction).

- Scott McGee has found a method that has helped his clients who reverse EFT to stop doing so. "Earlier this year I had a client arrive in a highly agitated state. Using MET tapping they were able to become calm (0 on a scale of 0-10). Yet when I asked if they could reconnect with their previous emotional state they very quickly became highly agitated again. I had them repeat the tapping and they were again able to become calm (0 on a scale of 0-10). Then I had them start tapping while they tried to become agitated again. We continued through all the meridian points. The result was that they were unable to reconnect to their highly agitated state."

APPENDIX F—SPIRITUAL EMERGENCY (SEN) CATEGORIES

The categories below are taken from Stanislav and Christina Grof's book *Spiritual Emergencies: When Personal Transformation Becomes a Crisis*, 1989. It is a groundbreaking book and we highly recommend it, as it defined and organized the whole field.

Definition of Spiritual Emergency:

Episodes of unusual experiences that involve changes in consciousness and in perceptual, emotional, cognitive, and psychosomatic functioning, in which there is a significant transpersonal emphasis in the process. It includes the ability to see the condition as an inner psychological process and to approach it in an internalized way. The capacity to form an adequate working relationship with a spirit of cooperation with people trying to assist is present.

The whole personality is usually affected. Often the person will share a "fear of going crazy". The above criteria exclude people with severe paranoid states, persecution delusions, hallucinations, and those who consistently use the mechanism of projection, exteriorization, and acting out.

Common Emergence Typologies

1. **Kundalini Awakening:** Powerful psychological and physical experiences especially involving physical sensations such as variations in body temperature, experiences of energy streaming up the spine, tremors, shaking, spasms, complex twisting movements, visions of lights, involuntary vocalizations, crying, acoustic phenomena, as well as emotional and psychological upheaval.

2. **Shamanic Crisis:** Dramatic episode of a non-ordinary state of consciousness often concurrent with a life threatening illness or trauma. There is an emphasis on physical suffering and encounter with death followed by rebirth and elements of ascent. Usually contact with totem or power animals, confrontations with demons, descent to the underworld where guidance is received followed by an ascent to the upperworld. ? ASTRAL TRAVEL

3. **Psychological Renewal through Activation of the Central Archetype:** Episode of psychological upheaval usually with strong psychotic processes. An inner experience of perceiving oneself as being in the middle of a world process (i.e. fighting for the survival of the human race). Emphasis on themes of death, afterlife, return to the beginnings of creation, cataclysmic clashes of opposites or polarities such as good/evil, male/female, and Christ/Devil.

4. **Psychic Opening:** Experiences may include telepathy, clairvoyance, precognition, psychokinesis, out-of-body travel, visions, synchronicities. In acute episodes the individual is flooded with psychic information, overwhelming the ego.

5. **Karmic Pattern or Past-Life Memories:** Dramatic experiences that seem like past life times or birth events. Can be intense emotional experiences of birth, torture, death, memories of family members or ancient cultures. Often these episodes illuminate present life difficulties: irrational fears, habits, or difficult interpersonal dynamics.

6. **Possession:** Least understood and most controversial type of spiritual emergency. Episode when the individual assumes the facial characteristics, gestures and attitudes of someone else typically diabolical in nature. Individuals can feel victimized or invaded or controlled with corresponding fear and concern.

7. **Channeling and Communication with Spirit Guides:** Includes instances of communication with unseen, non-hostile beings and involves participation in a trance state that allows other entities,

beings, or intelligences to speak. These entities characteristically have radically different voice and facial expressions that the individual normally has. Includes communication with spirit guides.

8. **Unitive Consciousness:** Experiences of inner and outer unity or harmony, strong positive emotions, transcendence of time and space, sense of sacredness, paradoxical nature, objectivity and reality of the insights, ineffability, and positive after effects. Can be prolonged and involuntary causing concern in others, sometimes even leading to inappropriate treatments such as electroshock.

9. **Near Death Experiences:** Involving up to 8% of the US population. Common pattern involves feelings of peace, followed by a transitory buzzing at which point one may find oneself viewing his body from above, followed by sensing a benign presence. Presence often induces individual to review his life and a decision to return to earthly life is made, terminating the episode. Other elements are common.

1. **Encounter with UFO's:** Typically a person experiences some form of communication, close contact, or abduction by alien beings perceived as originating on another planet. Can range from pleasant, inspiring, and even welcome to radically invasive, involuntary encounters which leave their victims filled with terror.

Precipitants

*   Spontaneous (rarely, usually signs such as dreams)

*   Threats to one's life (i.e. serious illness, accidents, operations)

*   Extreme physical exertion or prolonged lack of sleep

*   Perinatal events (i.e. childbirth, miscarriage, abortion)

*   Powerful sexual experiences

*   Powerful emotional experiences (e.g. loss of close relationship)

*   Series of life failures

*   Deep involvement in various forms of meditation or other spiritual practices (most common)

Treatment Guidelines

*   Provide psychospiritual framework

*   Little or no medication

*   Sanctuary over a hospital

*   Decrease or discontinue spiritual practice

*   Dietary changes

*   Exercise / body therapy

*   Contact with nature

Post Episode Functioning

Symptoms last minutes, and up to months; acute onset during three months or less (Lukoff)

Functioning enhanced after most intense period is complete over previous level of functioning (Lukoff and Grof). Typically more creative, more oriented to service, new parts of self activate (Turner).

APPENDIX G—THE INNER PEACE PROCESS (IPP)

The Inner Peace Process

Revision 1.1, March 2004
Copyright 2004 by Grant McFetridge

Welcome to our work at the Institute for the Study of Peak States!

We'll briefly cover in this manual the theory and application of the process. We've designed this process to be as simple as possible. However, to do this we had to accept that it wouldn't work for everyone. At the present time, the procedure you have in your hands is somewhere between 1/2 and 2/3 effective. By this, we mean that in any 100 people, you can expect that from 50 to 66 people will actually acquire the full state of 'Inner Peace'. Folks who don't may need more time with the process, or individual attention, or in some cases we can't help them at this time with this simple procedure.

A video on the Inner Peace Process is available. It covers what is in this handout. The first 30 minutes covers the theory of the process, and the last hour and thirty minutes actually shows an audience in a group setting using the process. It's designed to be used at home like an exercise video - you just follow along, making it more convenient for many people. It can be purchased via our website at www.PeakStates.com.

Potential Risks

After three years of testing with large groups of people, we haven't found any unusual problems with the process. Having said that, there is always a risk in using a new procedure, and **if you are unwilling to accept any and all of the consequences to using this process, then you must stop and not use this process. By using this process, you are accepting this risk, and we are not legally liable for your choice to do so or any consequences that may arise.**

We have identified three difficult experiences that you should be aware of:

1. By the nature of the process, it brings up uncomfortable feelings and body sensations during the process. This is to be expected, and they should go away with the use of the Emotional Freedom Technique (EFT) procedure as you proceed. If you have trouble making the feelings go away, we suggest you either study the EFT process at www.emofree.com, or find a therapist who knows the EFT process. In any case, these feelings that have come up during the process and couldn't be eliminated with EFT will eventually subside without treatment, although you won't get the benefit of the process or enter the Inner Peace state.

2. Rarely, by using this process you may acquire even better and more dramatic states of consciousness. These states are ones of increased health and wellbeing, but they may give you experiences and

abilities that you've never had before. Typically, in a few days you will become comfortable with these new states of being.

3. Some percentage of the public who successfully enter the Inner Peace state may lose the state later. Returning to 'average' consciousness can be experienced as somewhat difficult and unpleasant until they get used to it again. These people may feel depressed or upset returning to the kind of consciousness they always had before. Rerunning the procedure or using the other suggestions in this manual will usually restore the state. As we create improvements, we'll make them available via our website at www.PeakStates.com.

For More Information

For more in-depth information, please go to our website www.PeakStates.com. When we publish or create new procedures we'll keep you updated via our website.

Thanks for participating in our work!

All our best to you,

Grant McFetridge and the staff at the Institute for the Study of Peak States

November 2002
Hornby Island, British Columbia, Canada
www.PeakStates.com

PEAK STATES OF CONSCIOUSNESS

Understanding Peak States of Consciousness

Have you ever noticed that some people just seem to be happier, healthier, more successful, able to weather life's ups and downs more easily? In the current psychological paradigm, it's believed these people had better childhoods, had fewer traumas, better genetic backgrounds, nicer friends, and so on. In this model, it boils down to two factors - better genes or a better environment. And recently a third element has been added, better prenatal care. Although these elements are important, the main reason why some people live an amazing life independent of outside circumstances is outside of psychology's current paradigm.

In the 1960s, Dr. Abraham Maslow identified moments where people feel remarkably better. He called these moments 'peak experiences'. It turns out that one can have these peak experiences continuously. We refer to these long-lasting wonderful experiences as 'peak states' of consciousness. People who live in these wonderful states most or all of the time are exceptional people. It's not their personality that makes the difference, it's the state they're in! We've identified 15 major states so far, with a variety of substates and combination states. Any one of them is remarkably better than average consciousness. Without them, people deep down inside don't really feel like life is worth living, and they spend their lives in culturally approved ways that don't get them what they really want, since our culture doesn't even recognize the existence of these states. Each of the states has different fundamental characteristics that are the same for everyone.

Peak States and Psychological Healing

In the last few years, a number of very powerful and fast healing modalities have been invented, called as a group "power therapies". These processes are transforming the way that psychological healing is done worldwide. Using these or other therapies can remove specific, identifiable problems that you (or your client) have. The basic Whole-Hearted Healing (WHH) process is one of those very powerful therapies, and can be learned for free from our website, www.PeakStates.com. However, WHH was actually developed for a very different purpose. We were working on the problem of how to achieve permanent peak states of consciousness. Instead of trying to heal people so they could function normally, what we really want to do as healers and therapists is to bring people into states of consciousness where they not only are free of most of the issues people suffer from, but are living a life that is exceptional. To use an analogy, it's like most people are in hell with a bunch of pitchforks in them. They've been there so long it feels normal. Power therapies can take the pitchforks out, which is good, but leave them still in hell. What we wanted to do is find easy ways to move them out of hell and into heaven on earth.

If you decide you want to learn more about our Institute's work, and perhaps contribute to improving and discovering new processes, we recommend you learn a variety of these 'power therapies', especially the basic WHH process, so that you can gain an understanding of the psyche and a fundamental research tool that we use to work on the peak states project. Most of our work in the area of peak states of consciousness builds on this material. More advanced material not yet available on the website is in our book *Peak States of Consciousness*, Volumes 1 to 3.

Types of Peak States

There are two distinct groups of peak states. The group that's the most relevant for this pamphlet involves fusion between the multiple brains in the triune brain system. To explain, the brain is divided into three distinct biological parts - in everyday terms, the mind, heart, and body. What isn't commonly known is that for most people, the brains are separated and individually self-aware. To illustrate this from an everyday experience, you might recall being attracted to someone (the body brain's reaction), whom you didn't like (the heart brain's reaction), and feeling very confused about the situation (the mind brain's reaction).

For a certain class of peak states, these awarenesses can 'fuse' or 'merge' together, which means the brains involved lose their individuality and become a single awareness. Which brains merge and to what degree determines a number of different states. A 'Perry Diagram' can be used to explain the different types of brain states. It's drawn as a vertical row of circles whose overlap and distance from each other indicate the degree of fusion of awarenesses among the brains. Below is a very brief description of several of these brain fusion states. The first state on the list is the one the Inner Peace Process is designed to give you, but in rare occasions one or more of the others can occur from doing this procedure. Thus, we've included a description of ones that might occur when you use our process:

- **Inner Peace (Mind-heart fusion)**—You have an underlying feeling of calm no matter what you're feeling, hence its name of 'Inner Peace'. This state causes past traumas to no longer feel emotionally traumatic. Your emotional reactions are dictated by present circumstances and not by past trauma. Interestingly, when you do healing and get a temporary sensation of calm, peace, and lightness (CPL) afterwards, it's actually a momentary experience of this or an even better state.

- **The Beauty Way (Aliveness)**—This combination state includes the Inner Peace state, and additionally gives a feeling of 'aliveness' and a lack of negative judgment about people as well as an automatic knowledge of spiritual truths. Everything has a sort of beauty to it, hence the state's name. The 'noise' of 'mind chatter' in the head goes away.

- **Underlying Happiness/loving (Body-heart fusion)**—This state gives a permanent feeling of happiness that doesn't go away no matter what else you feel. In men, it's mostly happiness, in women it mostly feels very loving.

- **Brains Communicate**—You can communicate between your mind, heart and body just as if there were three children talking to each other inside of you.

- **Hollow (Mind-heart-body fusion)**—The interior of your body suddenly feels like it's made of air but still surrounded by skin. Activities get very effortless. In some cases, the skin boundary feels like it also disappears (which is yet another state not related to the fusion of the brains).

- **Inner Brightness**—You experience the interior of your body and head as filled with bright, white or golden light.

Peak states that don't have anything to do with brain fusion are covered in Volume 2 of the textbook *Peak States of Consciousness*. If you're curious, you can also check the www.PeakStates.com website for brief descriptions of these other states.

THE INNER PEACE PROCESS

Benefits of the 'Inner Peace' State

In the Inner Peace state, the client comes emotionally into the present moment. This means that all your past trauma suddenly stops feeling traumatic, no matter how hard you try to evoke feelings from the past. You now have an underlying sense of peace and calmness, and your emotions are in proportion to whatever is happening to you—you've lost your emotional 'buttons'. Since the vast majority of people's daily problems are created by past emotional traumatic material surfacing into the present, you can imagine how much better they would feel if they were in this state. Although this is true of everyone, it's particularly true of people suffering from a number of emotionally based issues. Rather than try to fix individual emotional issues one at a time, this process just turns *all* of them off all at once. You can imagine that applicability to a therapy practice. We suspect that certain trauma-based physical problems would also go away while the client is in the state. This is an area we're just now exploring. Please let us know of any of your results, and we'll post this information on the www.PeakStates.com website.

Clients don't find the change disturbing or unusual when they enter the Inner Peace state, as it's characterized more by an absence of problems, rather than an addition of new experiences and abilities as can happen with other states. We've also had enough experience with it now to consider it relatively free of side effects.

Why the Process Works

What causes the Inner Peace peak state to occur? In the Inner Peace state, the mind and the heart are fused together into one consciousness. It turns out that the Inner Peace state will generally be present in people continuously from birth if they experienced conception without trauma. Unfortunately, regressing someone to this developmental event trauma in order to give them the state is relatively difficult and time-consuming, making it too difficult for the average therapist to do in an office setting in a reasonable time. Instead, we've come up with a shortcut that still gives a great many people the Inner Peace state. The tradeoff here is speed and ease of use versus the number of people who will achieve the state. Since energy therapies are used to release the conception trauma with this process, another disadvantage to this fast and simple process is the small chance that the process may come undone sometime in the future.

The shortcut works by taking a critical moment in this developmental event, and describing the biological activity at that moment as a phrase in English. (Translations into other languages work, but the wording is critical and just using a translation dictionary may or may not be successful.) In this case, the phrase is "Join forces in Glory." I know that the phrase sounds strange and rather religious - but it is the best fit to the underlying biological process. We also include a visualization and music in the process to make it work more quickly and thoroughly. The music is similar to something that can be 'heard' at a spiritual level during conception. Likewise, the visualization is similar to a process that actually occurs during conception. Some people actually hear the 'real' music and see the 'real' experience the visualization is trying to portray during the process. Understanding what causes peak states, and how we derived the particular developmental event, phrase, music, and visualization is beyond the scope of this manual, but is part of the advanced Whole-Hearted Healing training available through the Institute for the Study of Peak States. We have the client repeat the phrase, or listen to it, while they visualize and listen to music. This puts the client back to the trauma at the correct moment, generally without their conscious awareness, and emotional and physical symptoms that occurred during their conception start coming into their bodies. As this happens, we have them use meridian therapies like EFT (Emotional Freedom Technique) to eliminate the trauma symptoms.

The Inner Peace Process Steps

Liability

If you are reading this manual and use this process on yourself, by doing so you have implicitly agreed to these liability and responsibility conditions below. If you are working with clients, we suggest you start the process by getting a written liability agreement. You must make totally clear to your client that this is a new, experimental process, and has no historical basis upon which to determine long-term effects or consequences. The client must be willing to take complete responsibility for whatever effects might happen, even though we have no idea what they might be, or how to fix them. Again, they need to understand that you and by extension the Institute are not responsible for consequences from the use of this process. Although we've been testing the process and have encountered no unusual problems, this doesn't mean that you or your client won't have something unexpected happen.

Step 1: Choose Past Emotional 'Indicator' Traumas

Pick three or four major past emotional traumas, ones the client can easily feel. WRITE THEM DOWN, else it is likely that you'll forget what they were. Rate the pain you feel in the present when you think about them on a scale of 0 (no pain) to 10 (the maximum possible pain). These are your indicators of how completely you are entering the state. When you're fully into the state, these 'indicator' traumas will have a rating of 0. Generally what happens is that people gradually move into the state, and this is reflected by the trauma ratings going down as you work. Note that we don't want you to use EFT or TAT on the traumatic memories themselves - we just want to have you pick traumas to use as measurement tools to see if you've entered the state. The pain will go away on these and all the other traumas that you didn't pick roughly simultaneously.

Step 2: Play the Required Music

The music is Beethoven's Fifth Symphony, first movement, (although we're working on a better choice of music). This particular piece of music is important, don't substitute. Unless you're incredibly lucky, choosing other music will not help and will probably interfere with the process. The music is played continuously during the process, and greatly helps evoke feelings and speed things up. Occasionally, a client may say that the music is disturbing to them, but this generally means the traumatic material from the conception experience is coming to consciousness and is to be expected in some people. Occasionally, due to negative cultural experiences such as with forcible assimilation of minority groups into the Western culture, clients might reject the music. Explaining how the music was chosen, and that other choices from different cultures could be used if someone knew how, can help here.

Step 3: Do a Visualization

As the process is run, you should try to visualize a chain with large links about a foot in diameter, running vertically though the body. Have the client imagine the chain is linking and unlinking in their body. The chain looks a bit like the large rings that a magician links and unlinks during a magic trick. It turns out that this visualization is what is actually occurring at a certain level of consciousness, and a good percentage of clients will be able to perceive this as it happens. When the process is done, the chain will be linked up and the client who could see the rings will find that they can no longer imagine it unlinking. This part of the procedure isn't critical; if you forget to do the visualization the process should still work reasonably well.

Step 4: Say the Required Phrase

While you are doing the procedure, you will repeat over and over the simple phrase "Join forces in glory." Don't change the wording - it's critical that you repeat it just as it's written. We realize that after a while, it gets really boring, but the phrase and music are critical parts of the process.

Step 5: Use EFT

You will be using the Emotional Freedom Technique (EFT) process on yourself to heal the feelings and sensations that will arise as you do the process (although any meridian therapy would probably work adequately). You will simply repeat the phrase over and over while you tap on meridian points while listening to the music, and if you can, do the visualization. The tapping process is shown on the video, or can be learned by getting the EFT manual from www.emofree.com. In a group setting, have everyone tap and repeat the phrase in unison. We've found a few people need to start each round of the music (and in some cases, each round of tapping) with the psychological reversal phrase "Even though I feel like I will die if I do this, I deeply and completely love and accept myself" while rubbing the 'sore spot', to have the EFT work. If you don't experience any change in sensations or feelings while the process is running, you may need to include all of the EFT steps. If you don't know them, review the manual or seek out an EFT practitioner. We've found that having someone tap on you as you do the process can increase your chance of having the EFT process work - remembering where to tap can distract you from feeling the sensations and emotions that should arise. For those of you who are working alone, practice EFT on yourself beforehand with other issues until the process itself doesn't distract you from what you're trying to heal.

Step 6: Run the Process

The procedure will almost certainly cause you to feel discomfort, both emotionally and physically. Rather than this being a problem, it's a sign that the process is working! You need to deliberately focus on and feel the discomforts, pains, and emotions, rather than try to avoid them. The EFT is used to eliminate the feelings, new ones arise, are eliminated, and so on until no more arise. The process won't work if you successfully ignore any symptoms that arise. Note that a number of people try to explain the arising sensations as due to what's going on in the classroom. For example, you might feel the choice of music is bad, or too loud, or that you need to leave to take care of some business, and so on. This can fool you and block the process from working, because you are not focusing on your feelings while you're doing the process.

Step 7: Check Your Progress

At the end of every few rounds of the music, check to see if your rating of your indicator traumas has gone to zero. (Remember, DON'T think about your indicator traumas while doing the process, or you might find that you've healed those few traumas accidentally. If you're not in the Inner Peace state all your other life's traumas will still be painful.)

Step 8: Continue Until There Are No Additional Changes

Generally, the process takes a minimum of 30 minutes, and can take up to 4 hours. You will need to continue the process even after your indicator traumas all go to zero. For most people, change will continue to happen. You continue the EFT for at least a couple of rounds of tapping past any additional changes in your body sensations, and preferably go an entire round of music with no additional changes. Not going long enough *is the single biggest mistake* people make. Since you've had the traumatic feeling from conception for your entire life, you consider the trauma sensations in your body to be normal. Thus you generally don't realize that you do have symptoms that you need to continue tapping on until they go away. Several hours of tapping spread over a couple of sessions works fine, and in fact can be required to get the full change that can happen. Continuing in this way also makes you less likely to fall out of the state.

If the Process Doesn't Work

What happens when you (or your client) thought it over, got excited by the possibilities, was willing to try this process, and it didn't work? Generally, you (or they) may feel like they are intrinsically defective, or doomed never to get what so many other people have. THIS IS NOT THE CASE! These and other peak states are actually everyone's birthright, and the reason why a particular individual does or does not have the state has nothing to do with their intrinsic ability or worthiness to have it. You (they) have just been unlucky in accumulating life experiences that block the state, and it will require more detective work to find out what else needs to be healed. Or you will have to wait until we come up with better procedures. However, there are other reasons why some people don't have peak states, and the Institute is currently investigating this problem.

For improvements and updates on this technique, please check in on the www.PeakStates.com website occasionally. We also suggest that you sign up for our very infrequent newsletter to be notified of new material. Additionally, if you are interested, there is an email group for people using the basic Whole-Hearted Healing (WHH) process which is particularly useful for healing pre-birth traumas like conception, and you can sign up by going to the website section on the WHH process. Here are some specific things to try:

- Try putting a combination of the essential oils spearmint and juniper berry on your 'karate chop' point while you're doing the process. That point is at the edge of your palm, and one of the EFT tapping points. Be sure to not get it in your eyes, it stings!

- You might need someone else to tap on you, or you may need to use the full EFT process. You might want to visit an EFT practitioner to get assistance.

- Try another power therapy in addition to the EFT, like the Tapas Acupressure Technique (TAT), Be Set Free Fast (BSFF), Eye Movement Desensitization and Reprocessing (EMDR), and so on.

- You might have been ignoring the sensations in your body while tapping. EFT won't work if you don't consciously place your attention on your body and emotions that arise.

- You may have forgotten to tap while doing the process. Just saying the phrase, listening to the music, and doing the visualization only accesses conception trauma - the EFT tapping is what eliminates it.

- If your birth language isn't English, you may have to translate the phrase into your birth language. This may not work, as the translation might not be accurate enough.

- You might have a 'dominant' trauma. In this case, there is some major issue going on in your life that is holding you out of the state. Further work with any powerful healing modality to eliminate the issue is required. Fortunately, the Inner Peace process that you've done wasn't wasted, as now that state will occur when the dominant trauma is eliminated. In other words, you will return to the Inner Peace state when those major traumas are healed, instead of the 'average' consciousness that you were used to.

- Some people still won't respond to this process. They might need to work with a professional who can help them access and heal the conception trauma directly. This sometimes works, and gives the better Beauty Way state as an added bonus - although usually it's something else in their life that is blocking the state. As we improve the process, we'll issue updates on the www.PeakStates.com website.

- A variety of organizations have processes that can induce peak states, albeit usually temporarily. If the Inner Peace Process was unsuccessful, or if you would like to add other peak states, you might try these other processes. Our website, www.PeakStates.com, has links to the ones that we know work at least for some people. Probably the easiest and simplest one is taught by Jacquelyn Aldana in her book *The 15 Minute Miracle*. In the future, we will be releasing more peak state processes, and you can find out about these by checking in with our website or signing up for our infrequent newsletter.

Recovering the Inner Peace State If You Lose It

For the people who moved into the Inner Peace state during the process, most will find that this state is relatively stable. Others may leave it for brief periods when some current stressful situation occurs, but they go back into the state as soon as the situation ends or they relax a bit. However, some people leave the state and it doesn't return. Their calmness leaves them, their traumatic past returns, and they go back to what they had before. This latter case can be a problem as they've had a chance to experience life in a better way and don't feel very good about living as they used to. For this group, we have some advice that will help most to get their state back:

- Do EFT or WHH or a hybrid combination on whatever issue drove you out of the state. You will generally pop back into the state once this issue is resolved.

- Repeat the Inner Peace process. If the process again works, you've probably left the state because the healing effects of the EFT became undone, or you didn't run the process long enough. This may be because your breathing was done in a way that reverses the effect of EFT. You can read about the correct way to breathe by reading Gay Hendricks *At The Speed of Life*. Another way to reverse the effects of EFT is by encountering a substance your body reacts to, called an 'energy toxin'. Review Gary Craig's manual or see an EFT practitioner for help in these areas.

- Focus on any negative judgments against self or others that occurred when you lost the state. Focusing on letting them go, or using a power therapy to help you do it, generally will pop you back into the Inner Peace state quite quickly. *This is the most successful method of returning to the Inner Peace state.*

Suggested Reading

Grant McFetridge, *Peak States of Consciousness*, (Volumes 1 and 2), Institute for the Study of Peak States Press, 2003.

Gary Craig, *Emotional Freedom Techniques: The Doorway to the New Healing Highrise: The Manual* (third edition), 1999. See www.emofree.com for a copy.

Acknowledgments

The breakthroughs needed for this process came from the dedicated hard work of the following people: Grant McFetridge, Wes Gietz, Dr. Deola Perry, Dr. Marie Green, and Dr. Mary Pellicer. Thanks also to the numerous volunteers who worked with us to test out these ideas over the years.

APPENDIX H—BIBLIOGRAPHY AND WEBSITES

Introduction to Power, Energy, and Meridian Therapies

- Articles on power and energy therapies at www.psychinnovations.com.

- Jim Durlacher's *Freedom From Fear Forever: The Acupower Way to Overcoming Your Fear, Phobias and Inner Problems,* 1997.

- Fred Gallo's *Energy Psychology: Explorations at the Interface of Energy, Cognition, Behavior, and Health*, CRC Press, 1998, at www.energypsych.com. One of the first survey books in this field.

- Association for Meridian Therapies in the UK, www.meridiantherapies.org.uk.

Specific Energy and Meridian Therapies

- EFT (Emotional Freedom Technique) - A simple and extremely effective energy therapy at www.emofree.com. Free download of the manual.

- BSFF (Be Set Free Fast), www.besetfreefast.com - A simple, effective, and even faster energy therapy than EFT.

- TFT (Thought Field Therapy) power therapy; www.tftrx.com - The original energy therapy.

- TAT (Tapas Acupressure Technique) power therapy: www.tat-intl.com - Specifically designed for allergies as well as trauma.

Other Power Therapies

- The TIR (Traumatic Incident Reduction) power therapy; www.tir.org; Gerald French and Chrys Harris, *Traumatic Incident Reduction (TIR)*, 1999.

- The EMDR (Eye Movement Desensitization and Reprocessing) power therapy: www.emdr.org; Francis Shapiro and Margot Forrest, *EMDR: The Breakthrough Therapy*, 1998.

- VKD (Visual Kinesthetic Dissociation). Leslie Bandler, *Solutions: Practical and Effective Antidotes for Sexual and Relationship Problems*, 1985.

Other Therapies

- Primal Psychology Page (the International Primal Association plus others) http://home.att.net/~jspeyrer, or www.primals.org. Contains a variety of links.

- The Hendricks Institute, www.hendricks.com; Hendricks Body Centered Therapy: Gay and Kathlyn Hendricks, *Learning to Love Yourself: A Guide to Becoming Centered*, 1982. *At the Speed of Life: A New Approach to Personal Change Through Body-Centered Therapy*, 1993.

- The Focusing Institute, www.focusing.org; Eugene Gendlin, *Focusing (Revised Edition)*, 1981.

- Foundation for Human Enrichment, the Somatic Experiencing therapy, www.traumahealing.com

- Ronald Davis, *The Gift of Dyslexia: Why Some of the Smartest People Can't Read and How They Can Learn*, 2002.

- Zivorad Slavinski's PEAT and DP-3 processes at www.spiritual-technology.com. It is both a peak state process and eliminates fundamental conflicts or 'games' at a deep level. His book is *PEAT and Neutralization of Primordial Polarities - Theory and Practice,* 2001.

Physical and emotional healing at a distance (no guarantee of success)

- Harold McCoy and trainees at the Ozark Research Institute, www.ozarkresearch.org

- Vianna Stibal at www.thetahealing.com. *Go Up And Seek God,* 1998.

- Chilel Qigong, originated by Dr. Pang Wing, at the Huaxia Zhineng Qigong Clinic and Training Center, China

Pre- and Perinatal Trauma

- Emerson Training seminars, William Emerson, www.emersonbirthrx.com

- Early Trauma Treatment and Trainings, Terry Larimore, www.terrylarimore.com

- Association for Pre- and Perinatal Psychology and Health, www.birthpsychology.com

Regression Techniques

- Winafred Blake Lucas, *Regression Therapy; A Handbook for Professionals, Volume 1: Past-Life Therapy,* 1993. Volume 2: Special Instances of Altered State Work, 1993.

Schizophrenia

- The American Mental Health Association, Dr. McKenzie MD, www.drmckenzie.com. This site describes finding that the cause of schizophrenia is trauma, using conventional investigation methodology. An independent verification of our own discovery.

The Triune Brain

- Dr. Paul MacLean, *The Triune Brain in Evolution: Role in Paleocerebral Functions,* 1990.

- Grant McFetridge, *Peak States of Consciousness: Theory and Applications, Volume 1: Breakthrough Techniques for Exceptional Quality of Life,* ISPS Press, 2003.

- Joseph Chilton Pierce, *Evolution's End: Claiming the Potential of Our Intelligence,* 1992.

- Tom Brown Jr., *The Vision,* 1988.

- Harville Hendrix, *Keeping the Love You Find,* 1992.

- Arthur Janov, *The New Primal Scream: Primal Therapy 20 Years On,* 2000.

- Elaine de Beauport, *The Three Faces of Mind: Developing your Mental, Emotional, and Behavioral Intelligence,* 1996.

Shamanism

- Foundation for Shamanic Studies, www.shamanism.org; Michael Harner, *Way of the Shaman,* 1990.

- Sandra Ingerman, *Soul Retrieval: Mending the Fragmented Self Through Shamanic Practice,* 1991.

- Hank Wesselman, *Spiritwalker: Messages from the Future,* 1995.

- Tom Brown Jr.'s The Tracker School, www.trackerschool.com; a how to book, *Awakening Spirits* , 1994.

The Phenomenon of Holes

- Dr. Cory Sea, *Seawork: Radical Tissue Transformation*, 1996, www.omen.net.au/~corysea

- H. Almaas, *Diamond Heart, Book 1: The Elements of the Real in Man,* Diamond Books, Berkeley CA, 1987.

Spiritual Emergencies

- The Spiritual Emergence Network - treatment, referrers, and descriptions at www.ciis.edu/comserv/sen.html

- Canadian Spiritual Emergence Service for people in spiritual emergencies - treatment, referrers, references at www.spiritualemergence.net/pages/home.html

- Emma Bragdon, *The Call of Spiritual Emergency: From Personal Crisis to Personal Transformation,* Harper and Row, 1990. Generally better than her other book, it's written for a wider audience and has an excellent section on how to help for others in spiritual emergency.

- Emma Bragdon, *A Sourcebook for Helping People in Spiritual Emergency,* Lightening Up Press, CA, 1988. This is part of her Ph.D dissertation, and has good appendixes of support options.

- Stanislav and Christina Grof, (ed.), *Spiritual Emergency: When Personal Transformation Becomes a Crisis* , Jeremy P. Tarcher, 1989. This book is an excellent collection of essays by Grof, Assagioli, Laing, Perry, Kalweit, Sannella, Anne Armstrong, Kornfield, Ram Dass, and others. I found it especially useful because it describes spiritual emergencies that lie outside of the typology that the Grof's use. It also goes into the structure of SEN as an organization. It's the first book in the field, and as such it's the pattern for all of the others. Recommended reading.

- Christina and Stanislav Grof, *The Stormy Search for the Self: A Guide to Personal Growth through Transformational Crisis,* Jeremy P. Tarcher, 1990. It describes in great detail the variety and experiences possible in spiritual emergency. Its section on self help strategies is excellent. The bibliography is divided up into the types of experiences making it pretty useful.

- Bonnie Greenwell, *Energies of Transformation: A Guide to the Kundalini Process,* Shakti River Press, 1990. Part of a Ph.D dissertation, it focuses on Kundalini awakening, but has a tendency to throw in non-Kundalini stuff into the pot. Specific list of physical and emotional symptoms, and good excerpts from various people's experiences, especially well known spiritual teachers.

- Yvonne Kason MD, *A Farther Shore: How Near-Death and Other Extraordinary Experiences Can Change Ordinary Lives,* HarperCollins, 1994. The best I've seen of the more recent books, it's excellent on actual descriptions.

- Lee Sannella, *Kundalini—Psychosis or Transcendence?* The edition I have is published by H.S.Dakin Co, CA 1976, but a revised edition was published later. An older, not as relevant work. This contains a number of case studies, and a western physiological scientific approach to Kundalini that I quite enjoyed. He mentions the problem of ego inflation that in my experience is very common with Kundalini awakening, but which I haven't seen discussed elsewhere. This issue is particularly relevant because of the problems it causes for both the person in Kundalini awakening and for the helper.

Unusual Spiritual States

- Stanislav Grof MD, *The Cosmic Game: Explorations of the Frontiers of Human Consciousness*, 1998. LSD Psychotherapy, 1980. The Adventure of Self Discovery, 1988.

- D. E. Harding, *On Having No Head: Seeing One's Original Nature*, 2002. Describes losing the ego shell.

- Grant McFetridge, *Peak States of Consciousness: Theory and Applications, Volume 2: Acquiring Extraordinary Spiritual and Shamanic States*, ISPS Press, 2006.

- Dr. Raymond Moody MD, *The Light Beyond*, 1989 (on the Near Death Experience), *Coming Back: A Psychiatrist Explores Past-Life Journeys*, 1992. *Reunions: Visionary Encounters With Departed Loved Ones*, 1994, on communicating with the dead.

APPENDIX I—QUIZ SOLUTIONS

Quiz #1

1. **Is the loving oneself process healing by itself? (i.e., if you client's pain went away when you had them do it, is their problem healed?)**

   No. If the problem went away, it just stopped being accessed by the client, but will return. Other techniques need to be used to permanently heal the client's problem.

2. **What indicators do you use to know when a trauma is healed?**

   Several. The basic one is CPL - the client feeling calm, peace, and lightness (as if a backpack were removed) at the end of the healing.

   Another test is to see if they've healed is to have the client come back to the present, then quickly flash to the trauma moment. If they see any OBE image, even if it then goes in body, it means there is still some traumatic content to the trauma.

   If the trauma was a core one, later traumas that you skipped over will now be CPL. Check the starting, in the present original situation for CPL to see if you got it all (SUDS 0-10). The fact that the physical situation has not changed is irrelevant.

3. **Do you always need a phrase with WHH?**

   No. Often, for light traumas, it will flash in and out of awareness so naturally as the problem heals that the client won't even be aware of it. Or the client is already in enough of a peak state that the mind brain doesn't need that aid to release it's part of the trauma.

4. **Do you always need an image with WHH?**

   No. It does make the process easier, however. Some people who are primarily kinesthetic find the lack of an image isn't any drawback, as they easily can tell they're at a particular moment in the past, in or out of body even without the image.

5. **If you heal a trauma completely, and the clients presenting problem goes away, does this mean you are done the trauma sequence?**

   No. But it's quite likely. I usually have them love themselves for a few minutes to flush up any further images in the trauma stack. Check any later traumas in the stack to see if they've completely dissolved as another check.

   Sometimes you will want them to pay attention later to see if any of the feeling returns. But usually the client can feel a sort of nagging, something isn't right feeling from the hidden earlier trauma. Asking them if they feel pulled earlier in time usually works. I recommend continuing especially if you haven't gotten to some sort of physical injury.

6. **What is a very simple way to help your client heal while they're in the trauma?**

   Do the loving yourself technique on yourself.

7. If the client is doing WHH correctly, what is still the main mistake that clients still make?

Not going long enough. That's why we've included the 3 minute rule on the outline of the WHH process. Often, they don't realize what healed feels and so don't realize that their pain isn't 'normal' or 'just the way it is when you get old'.

8. Can you expect the client to feel worse or better while you are doing WHH than the level of pain they had when they came in?

Worse.

9. What is a simple way to get an image when working with physical injury?

Relax the client. Have them watch for the flash of an image appearing and disappearing when you abruptly and gently press into the damage area. Keep repeating the process until they have the image firmly in awareness.

10. When is the best time to heal, i.e. when you are feeling really good, or when you're feeling really bad?

When you are feeling really bad. Often, the client unconsciously makes their life as miserable as possible to recreate the level of intensity that the trauma had, in order to try and heal it. This strategy seldom works however, and wrecks people's lives.

It makes sense that when you're feeling good, you would consciously or unconsciously want to resist feeling bad, after all!

11. When you are in a conflict or problem with someone else, how to you tell if it's one of your traumas being activated?

If you don't feel calm, peaceful, and lightness at the same time you are having feelings about a situation, then the emotion is ALWAYS from old trauma in the past. No matter what your friends say about the situation! This test really applies to emotional content. Thus, your client may say they have tapped to calm, peace, and lightness (CPL), but are still sick or injured. There problem is often still related to traumatic material from the past, material that is not directly related to emotions, such as holes, generational trauma, etc.

Anther example: Anyone in the beauty way feels calm, peace, and lightness, but they can still act in dysfunctional ways driven by old trauma not directly related to the emotions. (But it's a darn sight better than normal consciousness!) These same people can still be affected at the level that DPR works at also, which is at bottom due to trauma also.

12. If your client doesn't heal during the session, what does it mean? (3 possible reasons).

- You have a similar trauma feeling even if you can't feel it unconsciously.

- You don't want the client to heal unconsciously.

- Your technique or your teaching of the technique wasn't adequate.

13. What are the characteristics of a completely healed womb memory?

If the trauma was a womb memory, the fetus will feel CPL, have internal brightness, and a feeling of being very large in every part of the body. There will be an absence of any physical pain or sensation. The fetus will feel 'whole' after healing. Being very large and bright after healing a trauma is characteristic of womb memories, and seldom occurs for traumas after birth.

14. Is the trauma 'stack' made up of similar memories or of similar emotions?

Similar emotions/feelings. The story can completely change, including sexes or circumstances. This fact is often not understood by the clients, so they reject telling you about the earlier memory as you work with them because they think it isn't 'relevant'. Telling them ahead of time can save a lot of work and time!

15. One of the implications of this work is that blind people have visual images of trauma. Has this been found to be true?

Yes. See the book Mindsight to read about this.

16. When might you use the no-breath technique?

It brings up birth traumas. We don't recommend you use it for this purpose, but rather to help clients who are stuck on birth memories, usually because unconsciously they can't bring themselves to feel the awful sensation of not being able to breath.

17. What is the key piece that helps the healing that is contained in the loving yourself technique (not the loving part)?

Acceptance.

18. Why does normal therapy involving remembering trauma not help the client?

As the client remembers the trauma, they repeat the original mistake of staying out of body.

19. What does feeling large at the end of healing a womb trauma mean (or a trauma later in life for that matter)?

It means the physical damage has been healed. Stay with the increase in size until there is not more change for a couple of minutes to be sure you got it all. The increase in size is particularly noticeable to clients while doing womb trauma.

20. Can you be large in some areas and small in other areas when doing womb healing? If so, what would this mean?

Yes. It means the damage has been healed in the areas where you are large, but not in the areas where you are small. Be sure to continue until they are uniformly large.

21. What problems should you warn your clients of that might occur after a session of basic WHH?

They are listed in the handout for clients, but to review: Tiredness, possibly lasting for a couple of days in the case of healing severe injury; Another trauma that is unrelated to the work you did coming to the surface as the one you did heal was a block to feeling the new one; Not finishing the trauma stack, and having a client feel worse than when they came in; Having an earlier memory just start to surface only enough to give them distressing physical symptoms; might uncover a hole or soul loss with distressing symptoms.

Thus, material uncovered but not healed could cause a lot of distress for a while. I tell the clients to contact me immediately if something like that happens, as some won't, figuring it might cost more or for other reasons.

22. Is loving yourself being conceited? Many clients think so. What would you say to them?

Loving yourself is NOT being conceited, and in fact it helps speed the clients healing or access to trauma material or letting go of trauma temporarily. I quote the answer Maarten gave to this question:

"Loving yourself is not more conceited than hating yourself. Loving yourself is very healing and expanding, soon your self-love will flow out to others. It's better to give yourself the love you need than to expect it from others. If you don't have positive regard for yourself, you won't be able to recognize other people's love for you. Love yourself and people will soon follow your good example and love you, too. Then you have more resources to love others also."

Adam added this: " It is accepting yourself for what you are, as what you are. It is, further, impossible to truly love another without loving yourself."

23. What is a helpful trick to get people to the correct phrase during a basic WHH session?

Use Gendlin's focusing approach to get the 'felt sense'; Tell the client to just keep talking about their body sensations in a stream of consciousness babble, looking for a train of thought that makes the trauma feel WORSE; say what the phrase would have been if the trauma happened in the present, and adjust the wording to fit the chronological age of the trauma; in one of the write-ups, I said put your attention on the head, but in the last few years I've found it more useful to put the attention into the belly to get the phrase; As Maarten put it, sometimes the key is putting what we want into terms the client can understand - "If this body sensation of yours could speak, what would it say?"; And relaxing and loving yourself.

24. What does feeling a body sensation that stops at the vertical midline of the body often mean? i.e., only on the right or left side. (Give it a guess. Not in the notes)

It means that the trauma is probably from a sperm trauma if it's on the right, and from an egg trauma if on the left. Of course, you could have been past conception and just got hurt on one side, but it's pretty clear that it's a pre-conception trauma if the pain just stops abruptly at the centerline.

Quiz #2

1. Are there any exceptions to the principle of wanting to skip memories to get the earliest one?

No. Sometimes it is necessary to heal a trauma partially or fully before one can go earlier, however. And sometimes there is more than one 'branch' to the trauma string, requiring the client to go to each earliest memory on each branch. (Revised 8/06)

2. If the client sees an old photo image or made up memory when they regress, do you run it or try to get a real memory?

Run it. The reason that the client had the memory surface is usually because it's close to the real trauma memory. As you work with it, the real memory usually comes to consciousness.

3. What does feeling of heat often mean during a healing session?

The physical injury is healing. For example, when you bruise your body the area feels hot. The same situation occurs when doing WHH.

4. If you see some kind of dark looking kind of structure in your body, what do you think it is and how do you fix it (2 different problems)?

- A Buddha brain structure - generally, it causes pain and/or organ dysfunction. Focusing on the Buddha above the head, with the ball of light or loving yourself technique will relatively rapidly dissolve it if you are in the correct trauma memory.

- It's a visual of a hole. If they can go into it, and/or it feels like a terrible deficient emptiness, that's what it is. Use the trick of pressure or going into the hole to find the original physical damage that caused it.

5. Does DPR fix the underlying trauma?

No. But fixing the underlying trauma will cause the 'cord' to dissolve.

6. After using DPR will the client's behavior change? Will yours?

Sometimes it will, sometimes it won't. However, your response to the client generally does, because the material you used to feel is now gone.

7. Does healing the underlying trauma eliminate energetic connections?

Yes, it eliminates the involuntary chords. Finding the right trauma is sometimes difficult, however. (Using advanced WHH makes this process easy, though. It involves looking down the cord and seeing the image of the generating trauma.)

8. What do you do if the trauma won't heal? List at least 4 things.

- Find what feeling they characteristically refuse to feel, and see if it's that one.

- Use the ball of white light technique.

- Use the loving oneself technique on the client.

- Have the therapist use the loving technique on themselves to calm own trauma.

- Have the client send heart chakra energy to the client and put up a barrier around them (advanced technique).

- Use WHH with the TAT approach, if circumstances of the trauma recall allow it.

- Try seeing if correcting for psychological reversal helps.

- Have them focus on any injury.

- Use hyperventilation (breathwork).

- Put them in the body position of the trauma, and have the same body motions.

- Use DPR on them.

- Put up a 'barrier' around them (an advanced technique).

- Make sure they have the CORRECT phrase, use stream of consciousness if there is a block (the symptoms should worsen as they get closer).

- Make sure they are in-body.

- Use patience and wait out the resistance.

- Check for copies or generational trauma.

- As appropriate, use another power therapy like EFT or TAT.

- Listen for and repeat over and over the Gaia command.

- Look at any similar trauma in yourself, or any unconscious reason you don't want them to heal.

- Use WHH and the TIR viewing process in conjunction, especially when the client does not feel any emotion with the trauma.

- Ask the client if they are really focused on some other issue.

- Especially for new clients, try healing something else that isn't very traumatic so that the client gets an experience of healing to check on their understanding of the method.

- Look for some feeling the client is unwilling to feel (ex. sexual, anger, nausea, joy). Particularly in birth trauma, look for resistance to feeling that they don't have enough air.

- If it is self healing work, try early in the morning just at waking.

- Use deep breathing either as a way of relaxing the diaphragm, or for extended periods of time to build up an oxygen surplus (all the way to hyperventilation and tetany if necessary).

- Use physical manipulation of the diaphragm to release it's tension, or use a motion of rising and falling on a surface to get the same effect (see 'Recent Improvements').

- Allow your belly to enlarge and move upward (advanced technique).

- If a hole is emerging into awareness, are they blocking feelings of terrible deficient emptiness?

- If soul loss experiences are emerging, are they blocking a sense of lack or loss?

- Make sure the client really understands what you mean by 'being in the body', and repeat the concept a variety of ways to make sure (i.e., "Move the 'camera' to the right or the left so you know that you can, now move straight into the body...", etc.).

- Check for related earlier and or later trauma that is causing this trauma to be suppressed.

- Make sure that the client is not judging what happened, acceptance is the key.

- Make sure that they are not 'loving themselves' by staying out of body, as in giving their past self a hug.

- Make sure they are accepting what happened and are not trying to change it.

- Make sure they are staying focused on the particular moment in time and are not jumping around in time, either during the trauma or to other traumas.

- Guess the emotion or phrase that might be blocked (i.e. "If someone else was in this situation, what might they feel?"

- Wait for another time to when the client is feeling more miserable about the issue, (which means they are closer to the original trauma and it will be easier to access).

- Wait for another day, perhaps something in the environment will help the block to weaken.

- Send them to another healer, particularly one already in a peak state.

9. **What are the 2 types of unusual problems that won't heal with just the standard WHH technique (the 8 step version)?**

Copies and generational trauma. A number of situations require you to understand the trauma that indirectly causes the problem before you can heal it, though. (Two problems that are beyond the scope of this class are issues around good and evil, and physical damage that requires regenerative healing also, such as cut spines).

10. **What do you do if a past life memory comes up while healing?**

You have a choice - you can heal it, or just go earlier to the trauma with a similar feeling (NOT a similar story usually!) from this lifetime. Sometimes the client unconsciously needs that practice before they can face it in this lifetime.

If the memory in this lifetime that feels similar doesn't come up fairly soon, heal the past life and look again. But if another past life comes up, it's pretty much a waste of time to heal that. Instead, focus on finding the trauma in this life. There is ALWAYS a trauma in this life driving the client to access the past life.

11. **Will your clients be grateful for the healing work you have done with them?**

Generally not. This is the apex problem that is a difficulty for all power therapies, in that they forget in a day or so that it was ever a significant problem. Instead, they start thinking about how miserable they are as a new trauma gets activated, and just assume that your work didn't do much good. In the future, lets see if we can't get our clients into a semi permanent peak state before the session is over!!!

12. As a therapist, what are the most important things you need to do with a client before starting the healing process?

Because of the apex problem, you need to write down the issue and how bad it is on a scale of 0 to 10. If you are charging only for cures, you need to get an agreement on what a cure constitutes for this client. Cover any liability and fee issues, and possibly mention any potential adverse reactions they might have later (See the sample sheet in your manual.)

13. Can your client or yourself get into trouble using WHH?

Yes. The client might not finish healing, an earlier memory might arise that involves material you can't help them with because your skill or level of healing is not great enough. Clients that are suicidal are ones to avoid if your professional setting and skill level are not adequate.

Another stranger reason can occur. The client can be so successful in healing, their body relaxes fully for the first time in a long time. They get so relaxed that they can't stay awake. The problem here is that they can get into a car accident on the way home! Have them take a nap in the office before they leave to avoid this problem.

14. What are the 2 different reasons during a healing session that a client may describe that they feel a lack or something missing, and what do you do about it?

I asked this question because the client's experience between the two choices is quite different, but the wording may come out similar if you don't specifically ask, "Is it a 'deficient emptiness' or a feeling of 'something lacking or missing'?

- Soul loss. Heal the underlying trauma, it's the one that you are on that allowed them to become aware of the loss. Make sure that it feels like something is missing is the sensation. After the trauma is finished, and if the 'loss' feeling is not gone, have them sing the first song that comes to mind. Alternately, have them hum or use a rhythmic chant if you can't get them to sing.

- The other possibility is holes. Ask them if it feels like a terrible, deficient emptiness. Find the location in their body, if necessary have them run their hand over their body to localize where the feeling is coming from. Then, have them go into the hole with their awareness (the 'I'), or use pressure to get the image of when that area was damaged.

15. If a memory has pleasant feelings, is this a trauma that also needs to be healed?

Yes, unfortunately, and every time in my experience (except for a feeling of underlying happiness, which is due to a peak state). This is usually because something bad happened, and the bad feeling is concealed under a good feeling. This might occur when you were feeling good and something bad suddenly and unexpectedly happened. One way to verify this is to find out if it has an OBE image with it.

16. How many biological brains do you have?

Three main brains, the mind (primate, cortex), heart (mammalian, limbic), and body (reptilian, R-complex, 'Hara' in Japanese); and two sub brains, the Buddha brain (frontal cortex) associated with the mind brain, and the solar plexus brain associated with the body brain.

17. If you have a trauma that is similar to your client's, will he be unable to heal with WHH?

No, but the outcome is less certain. The client may just ignore the fact that you are unconsciously freaking out, but then again it may cause them from healing. No telling which.

18. If you are in the 'Beauty Way", do you still make energetic connections via chords?

Yes. Even though you can't feel or easily access old trauma, you still run chords to other people because of your personality defenses (shell). Additionally, we believe that the cord mechanism is actually a normal one, that allows positive harmony not only between people, but between people and plants, for example. Unfortunately, due to people's shell and trauma material, the original purpose is lost.

19. Name a mechanism that causes people to get diseases.

- The body getting a disease that gives symptoms that are similar to the feeling of a trauma.

- A trauma interfering with the natural immune system function (a body decision), such as a decision to no longer live.

- A disease that the body associates with feeling better (ex. having parasites because they make the body feel less alone).

20. What are typical reasons your client can get really cold during a basic WHH session?

It usually means a fear reaction, and that often they are not aware of actually being afraid. Interestingly, I've also seen fear localized in the heart as a burning sensation. As one of you mentioned, it may also be a shock response, but I couldn't say without testing. Staying with it causes it to end, although it may take a number of minutes.

Actual physical cold during the trauma might also be the cause, as when the baby is born into a cold operating room.

21. If the fetus hears their mom or someone else say something during a physical trauma, can this be a problem? How about a very loud noise?

Yes. The organism can store the phrase in the mind in a kind of infinite playback loop, as if it were a tape that continuously ran through the tape machine. This causes the mind to have difficulties thinking, almost like there was a 'jangly' sensation in the mind. These phrases also can cause us to behave in weird ways, as we 'unconsciously' check them for guidance. Even worse, the mind can use them to cause pain to the rest of the organism as a control mechanism.

With loud noises, I've seen it cause severe tinnitus (ringing in ears), even though the event occurred in the womb. (I've also seen this due to soul stealing too, the voice repressed into the sensation of a noise in the ears.)

And of course if a loud noise is linked to a trauma, the moment must come to CPL even though the loud noise is still happening at that moment.

22. Can chords be located at different places in the body? Can you have more than one chord connected to a certain spot?

Yes for both questions.

23. Can there be different phrases in a specific trauma?

Yes. I haven't emphasized this in the papers, as I was trying to keep them as simple as possible. Thus, I you may see a new phrase in different areas of injury, even though they may have occurred simultaneously in a single trauma. And of course, there is a whole array of related phrases attached to the core phrase that occurs at the moment of trauma. Bringing these secondary phrases to consciousness releases them, but doesn't get them all at once like finding the core phrase. Only the core phrase really heals the trauma by inducing temporary merging of the brains.

24. Does the earliest image always have the exact feeling that the original problem that you started with had?

No. Again, I don't make any mention of this in the notes, as I tried to keep it all simple. You track the earliest feeling as far as it can go, then as you continue to go backwards in the stack you might find traumas with different sorts of feelings. They still connect to later ones, but it's due to an association that isn't always obvious in the beginning. However, if done to completion the client will understand the connection between the earlier trauma and the later ones. The TIR (Traumatic Incident Reduction) people have very good illustrations of this principle of traumas linking together. Sticking to the exact feeling is appropriate for eliminating the client's complaint, and going earlier to images that arise gets whatever core there may be.

25. Each brain thinks in it's own 'language'. What is the hearts 'language'?

It thinks in sequences of emotions, and uses images to control the other brains and access relevant traumas. I often tell clients that there are no good and bad emotions, that they are just a language, and that rejecting or resisting certain feelings is exactly like trying to speak without allowing yourself to use a lot of the words in the dictionary.

Quiz #3

1. **What do you tell a client to do who encounters a 'wire' or 'bottle' in their body during healing a trauma?**

   It's most probably a Buddha brain structure. Generally, it causes pain and/or organ dysfunction. Focusing on the Buddha above the head, with the ball of light or loving yourself technique while staying in the originating trauma will relatively rapidly dissolve it.

2. **Do you have to heal the correct trauma first before you can get a soul piece back?**

   No. Shamanic techniques will bring back soul pieces. However, we don't know if this is permanent. Healing the trauma is a permanent fix.

3. **What alternatives do you have if the client won't sing a song?**

   Humming, chanting. As odd as it seems, a lot of clients are too embarrassed to actually sing in your office for a variety of reasons. And having them just think about the song or recall the tune doesn't appear to be effective.

4. **If, during a healing, the client describes a cloud coming out of their bodies, what does this mean and what do you do?**

   This means that they're letting go of a 'stolen soul piece', to use shamanic terminology. It's very likely that they will bring it back in the future unless the underlying problem is solved, but that's part of the advanced WHH training.

5. **If, during a healing, the client describes seeing their own body walking away from them while they're still in their body in the trauma in the past, what does this mean and what do you do?**

   The client is actually witnessing soul loss. Have them hold the self inside their body while they heal the originating trauma. You can just heal the trauma without doing that, but the soul piece then has to either come back spontaneously or you have to use a song to do it.

6. **When is it appropriate to use a mixture of EFT and WHH with a client? Or just EFT?**

   Yes. However, we recommend resolving the ethical issues around using a procedure that we believe can be reversed. → III newsletter 13

7. **When is it not appropriate to use EFT or energy therapy with a client?**

   With material that if the healing came undone, the client would be at risk. For example, using EFT on a paralyzing fear of heights on a pilot would be such a case.

8. **What is the presenting symptom that we suspect often hides the ability to open and use the heart chakra?**

   Addictions. It looks like the underlying mechanism is a hole in the chest. Once it's healed, have the client witness *in utero* how they learned to use the chakra by watching their mother while in the womb.

9. **What do you do for a generational trauma?**

   Try TAT, it's fast and simple. Otherwise, regress the client to birth (or whenever) where the generational trauma is acquired, and have them follow it back from generation to generation to it's origin. It's very much like seeing a deck of cards, where each card is a generation. Heal it at the origin, and all subsequent traumas dissolve.

10. Or, heal the underlying trauma in the solar plexus that causes the generational trauma to be brought in.

For some clients, where do they feel the generational trauma comes from (a physical direction)?

Out in front and slightly upward from the solar plexus.

11. When is it especially useful to use the TIR 'viewing' of a traumatic sequence? (2 examples)?

- The client can't feel the emotional content of a trauma.

- There is trauma content over a period of time, for example rape or a car accident.

12. Is the phenomenon of 'shock' a problem with WHH?

No. Although it is a problem in other therapies, WHH does not seem to have difficulty with it. Occasionally, the client will get very cold with that sort of trauma (often a fear response), and putting them in a blanket works well.

13. Is WHH an energy, meridian, or other kind of therapy?

Other kind - it's a regression technique under the heading of a 'power therapy'.

14. Is depression a symptom of trauma?

There are several competing phenomenon lumped under the word depression. If it is a chronic emotion, such as debilitating sadness that causes the diagnosis of depression, then just heal it with WHH normally. If it is 'true' depression, it's like you have the terminal 'blahs' but can still feel emotions, although very muted. This needs to be healed by finding the phrase you are trying not to think. This will eliminate the depression, but WHH should be done on why the phrase was one that you didn't want to feel. (I would like to find a good method for finding the depression phrase, but I haven't yet.)

15. Is muscle testing reliable for trauma work?

Sometimes. Because the muscle testing is influenced by what the body has associated and by the feelings of people around the person being tested, it can become wrong or even deliberately misleading. However, on issues not in this category, it can also be stunningly accurate. Not knowing which kind of answer - correct or wrong - limits the usefulness of this technique. Also, certain kinds of problems will never get correct results, due to the imperative that the body brain obeys, to survive. Trying to solve these problems make the body feel like it's survival is threatened, so doing muscle testing on these issues is impossible.

16. Can TAT be permanent? Or is it reversible?

We're not sure. At the moment, we think it may be permanent in some cases, and reversible in others.

17. Are holes in people common or uncommon?

Very common. In fact, most people look like Swiss cheese with very little cheese. The majority of large holes are formed during birth or *in utero*. Occasionally, some people are all hole. These people have a certain type of problem well described by Cory Sea.

18. What are two ways people can harm or block each other from healing, but at a distance?

With chords, or by sending 'soul pieces'. There is another case, but it's beyond the scope of this class.

19. Do meridian therapies heal holes?

We don't know for sure, but we don't think meridian therapies can heal holes. This may be what allows meridian therapies to be reversible. More experimentation needs to be run.

20. When using EFT or other meridian therapy on a client's headaches, and they come back after a while, what does this mean and how do you fix it?

This is something I've observed over the years. It usually means there is a birth trauma that involves head injury, and the EFT isn't getting to the root problem. Regressing them to these severe injuries seems to do the trick. I haven't tried using EFT at that point in time on that sort of injury, but I bet it would be adequate now the client is at the correct trauma. I've seen the feeling of frustration is the theme for the trauma stack, at least for some people.

21. Why do we believe that the healing from using meridian therapies is potentially reversible?

From an experiment we ran, it looks very likely that it was possible to restore charge on a trauma that had the charge removed with EFT. Reverse breathing appeared to be an important step. The other reason is in the EFT literature itself. Clients can sometimes have specific traumas reverse when they are exposed to 'energy toxins' that they are sensitive to.

22. When doing DPR, is it OK to say "In fact, it's the client's problem that makes them so lovable, and in fact if they didn't have it they wouldn't be so lovable?"

Yes. This is exactly the kind of feeling we're trying to get to - it's actually unconditional love, and saying that they wouldn't be so lovable is just a trick to understand the level of the feeling we're trying to identify.

APPENDIX J—ADMINISTRATIVE FORMS

<u>Any Potentially Dangerous Health Conditions</u>

IF YOU HAVE ANY POTENTIALLY SERIOUS HEALTH PROBLEMS OR ISSUES (LIKE CHEST PAIN OR HEART CONDITIONS), LET US KNOW IMMEDIATELY AND LIST IT ON THIS FORM! We suggest that people with a heart condition NOT take the workshop, just in case (we will give a full refund). Also, if you have any physical conditions that might make these processes difficult to do, or might make your condition worsen, please let us know on this form (such as diabetes, back injuries, etc.). If this is the case, we expect you to work with your physician both before and after the workshop to be sure your condition doesn't worsen.

Personal List of Issues

Rate each issue on a scale of 0 to 10.
- **0** means there is no pain or intensity on the issue;
- **10** means this is the maximum pain or intensity you can imagine

Background Questionnaire

(Please complete the front and back, then tear out and hand in)

NAME:

_____

1. **Methodologies used:**
   (for each technique please indicate one of the following:
   No Training; Trained but don't use; Some use; Extensive use, any other comments)

   Reiki, Qigong, etc.

   _____

   Personal meditation

   _____

   Acupuncture, acupressure

   _____

   Shamanic techniques

   _____

   EFT, TFT, etc.

   _____

   EMDR

   _____

   TAT

   _____

   Other techniques

   _____

   Comments:

2. What professional reasons do you have for being here?

3. What personal reasons do you have for being here?

4. What are your hopes for yourself (personally or professionally) for being here?

5. What fears do you have about being here?

Disclaimer of Responsibility Agreement

(to be handed in)

Intent: The material that you will be learning is state of the art and still very experimental. Long-term effects, if any, have not been studied or researched. Thus, we cannot guarantee that you or the people you work with will not have some sort of adverse reaction that we did not anticipate. If you are not willing to take full and complete responsibility for what happens by using our material we require that you not start with the training or private session, and a full refund excluding deposit will be returned to you if one was made. This is all common sense given the nature of our material, but we want to make it perfectly explicit up front.

I (print name),
_____

located at the address,
_____

_____

do agree to the following:

- I take complete responsibility for my own emotional and/or physical well being both during and after this workshop or private session.

- As a therapist, I agree to instruct others whom I help with the Institute techniques to take complete responsibility for their emotional and/or physical well being.

- I agree to hold harmless **The Institute For The Study of Peak States,** anyone associated with the Institute now, in the past or in the future, and anyone else involved with these Institute techniques from any claims made by anyone whom I seek to help with these techniques including myself.

- As a layperson I will use the techniques under the supervision of a qualified therapist or physician as legally appropriate.

- As a therapist I will use the techniques only if I have previous adequate trauma therapy experience.

- I will not use these techniques to try to solve a problem where common sense would tell me that it is not appropriate.

- I understand that several of the processes and techniques in this class are proprietary or patent protected. I will use these with clients only after becoming certified by the Institute and signing a license agreement with the Institute.

Signed: _____   Date: _____

Witness: _____

<u>Disclaimer of Responsibility Agreement</u>

(student's copy)

Intent: The material that you will be learning is state of the art and still very experimental. Long-term effects, if any, have not been studied or researched. Thus, we cannot guarantee that you or the people you work with will not have some sort of adverse reaction that we did not anticipate. If you are not willing to take full and complete responsibility for what happens by using our material we require that you not start with the training or private session, and a full refund excluding deposit will be returned to you if one was made. This is all common sense given the nature of our material, but we want to make it perfectly explicit up front.

I (print name),

located at the address,

do agree to the following:

- I take complete responsibility for my own emotional and/or physical well being both during and after this workshop or private session.

- As a therapist, I agree to instruct others whom I help with the Institute techniques to take complete responsibility for their emotional and/or physical well being.

- I agree to hold harmless **The Institute For The Study of Peak States,** anyone associated with the Institute now, in the past or in the future, and anyone else involved with these Institute techniques from any claims made by anyone whom I seek to help with these techniques including myself.

- As a layperson I will use the techniques under the supervision of a qualified therapist or physician as legally appropriate.

- As a therapist I will use the techniques only if I have previous adequate trauma therapy experience.

- I will not use these techniques to try to solve a problem where common sense would tell me that it is not appropriate.

- I understand that several of the processes and techniques in this class are proprietary or patent protected. I will use these with clients only after becoming certified by the Institute and signing a license agreement with the Institute.

Signed: Date:

Witness:

Release of video and distribution rights

Basic Whole-Hearted Healing Training

Intent: We plan on video and audio taping the basic Whole-Hearted Healing workshop you are participating in. We hope to make this into demonstration videos and training material. By signing this document, you are giving us permission to use the video footage and sound that may include your participation. If there is any particular portion of the workshop that you don't want seen by others, you need to let us know the day it is filmed, else your permission is assumed. Please note that at the bottom of this form. Thanks!

I,

_____

located at the address,

_____

_____

do agree to releasing any rights to the material video or sound taped in this basic Whole-Hearted Healing™ workshop.

Signed: _____   Date: _____

Witness: _____

Information for Email and website practitioner lists

Please write down contact information (especially email addresses), and a short paragraph about yourself and your work. If you so desire, this will be put on our web site so that we can list you as a practitioner of WHH. If doing healing with others, on either a free or paid basis, is appealing to you, please do so as we constantly get requests from clients looking for people either in their area or on the phone they can work with. By writing a short paragraph (and JPEG photo if possible), you are introducing yourself to potential clients who need your help. May we suggest that you mention what kind of clients you prefer to work with, i.e. your specialty.

Name:
_____

Mailing Address:
_____

City, State, Zip
_____

Phone:
_____

Email:
_____

**Descriptive
Paragraph:**

Basic Whole-Hearted Healing

Workshop Evaluation

Please help us to improve this workshop and techniques by providing feedback on this form. Please indicate which instructor you are thinking or when you make comments. Provide examples where appropriate.

Please rate the following items by circling the appropriate response.

	Needs to improve	Could improve	OK	Very Good	Great!
1. Date and time	1	2	3	4	5
2. Location & facilities	1	2	3	4	5
3. Cost	1	2	3	4	5
4. Length of the workshop	1	2	3	4	5
5. Breaks	1	2	3	4	5
6. Clarity of presentations and examples	1	2	3	4	5
7. Pace	1	2	3	4	5
8. Teaching style	1	2	3	4	5
9. Response to questions	1	2	3	4	5
10. Coverage of topics	1	2	3	4	5
11. Flow and continuity	1	2	3	4	5
12. Manual	1	2	3	4	5
13. Overall rating	1	2	3	4	5

14. How did you learn about this workshop?

15. What were some good parts or aspects for you?

16. What would you change about the workshop?

17. Are there topics that should be covered more thoroughly? Which ones?

18. What benefit or impact did the workshop have for you?

19. Would you recommend this workshop to colleagues?

20. Please note any additional criticisms, suggestions for how to improve the workshop or other comments

APPENDIX K – STATE OF CONSCIOUSNESS EVALUATION QUESTIONNAIRE

Name: _____   **Date:** _____

Reason for questionnaire:
_____

1. Close your eyes. Get a sense of where "You" are inside you body, where your "Center of Awareness" is. It may help to point your finger at yourself starting at your forehead and working your way down your body. Stop when you get to the point that feels like that is where "You" are. "You" may be at one point or more diffusely spread out through a general region of your body. Indicate on the figure to the right the location of you Center of Awareness

2. Does your "Center of Awareness" extend out into the space around you?   ❑ Yes   ❑ No

3. Close your eyes and cover them with your hands. Notice how bright it is (the underlying uniform level of brightness—not areas of spots or colors.) Circle the most appropriate number to indicate this.

1	**2**	**3**	**4**
Totally black*			**Like bright sunlight**

* If totally black is it a fluorescent black, like your head is lit up with a fluorescent light.   ❑ Yes   ❑ No

4. Close your eyes. Think about nothing at all for about 1-2 minutes. Notice how much "mind Chatter" is present. Circle the most appropriate number to indicate this.

1	**2**	**3**	**4**
Constant chatter*			**Total quiet**

* This would be like sitting in a bar hearing all the talking in the background or perhaps like the constant hum of an air conditioner.

5. Pick 4 very emotionally painful incidents from your past. Write down a key phrase to identify each incident. Close your eyes and for each incident feel the emotional pain you experience right now when you think about it. Rate the intensity of the emotional pain on a scale of 0 (No pain, you feel calm peace and light) to 10 (the most extreme pain you can imagine).

#1 _____   0 1 2 3 4 5 6 7 8 9 10

#2 _____   0 1 2 3 4 5 6 7 8 9 10

#3 _____   0 1 2 3 4 5 6 7 8 9 10

#4	0	1	2	3	4	5	6	7	8	9	10

---

6. How many hours of sleep does it take before you feel rested?   _____ hours

---

7. **Question: Why are you alive?**   **Answer: Simply to live, no other reason**

Rate how much you agree or disagree with the answer to the question given above.

1	2	3	4
Disagree totally	Disagree somewhat	Agree somewhat	Agree totally

---

8. **Question: Why are you alive?**   **Answer: Simply to love, no other reason**

Rate how much you agree or disagree with the answer to the question given above.

1	2	3	4
Disagree totally	Disagree somewhat	Agree somewhat	Agree totally

---

9. Imagine that all your friends and family are dead. You are in a foreign country where you don't speak the language. There is no one you can call for help. Really try to put yourself into this situation for a moment and feel what it would be like. Now answer the questions below by circling the most appropriate number on the scale to the right.

		1	2	3	4
a.	Would you feel lonely?	Very lonely			Not at all lonely

		1	2	3	4
b.	Would you feel safe?	Not at all safe			Very safe

		1	2	3	4
c.	Would you feel anxious?	Very anxious			Not at all anxious

---

10. Pay attention to the inside of your body. Move your arms and legs; breathe. Notice if you feel sensations as your bones and muscles move or if you only feel like air inside, like you're hollow.

Rate your sense of hollowness.

NOTE: You may only have some parts that feel hollow, if so indicate what parts below.

1	2	3
Not hollow at all	Some parts are hollow*	Totally hollow

• List which parts are hollow:

_____

11. Pay attention to your skin. Does it feel like your body stops at the skin or like you have no skin boundary at all (like the air blows right through your body)?

Rate your sense of your skin boundary.	**1**	**2**	**3**
NOTE: You may sense only a partial skin boundary, if so describe what this feels like below.	**Total skin boundary**	**Partial skin boundary ***	**No skin boundary**

* List which parts without a skin boundary:

_____

Glossary

We've tried to use 'standard' psychological, shamanic or spiritual terminology whenever we can.

Apex phenomenon: Coined by Dr. Callahan, refers to the common occurrence after an issue is eliminated by a therapy that the client tries to explain the change by something they know, such as being distracted, even though the explanation doesn't fit. Has been extended to include the phenomenon of the client forgetting (to the point of disbelief) that the healed issue was ever a problem for them.

Applied kinesiology: Developed for chiropractic, uses changing muscle strength to test for various problems and sensitivities to toxins. Mistakenly assumes the body isn't self aware with it's own agenda. Same principle as muscle testing or dowsing.

Body: The reptilian brain, at the base of the skull. Thinks in gestalt body sensations. Experiences itself in the lower belly. Known as the hara in Japanese. Moves the OBE awareness around. Is the brain that we communicate when doing dowsing or muscle testing.

Breathwork: Using hyperventilation for extended periods of time to facilitate healing. A variety of types exist.

Brilliance State: A peak state made up of the 'Hollow' state and the 'Light' state. Experientially, the body feels like it's made of air with a skin boundary, and filled with bright clear (or slightly gold colored) light. All the brains fused.

BSFF - Be Set Free Fast: Invented by Larry Nims, a spinoff of TFT involving only 3 meridian points. Also important for the technique called Instant BSFF, where the process is programmed internally to occur at a cue word.

Buddha brain: The prefrontal lobes in the brain. Experientially it feels like a huge, massive statue of Buddha located above the head. Normally fused with the mind brain.

Buddha brain structures: Looking like cables or containers internal to the body, appearing like the movie idea of an alien implant. Created by the Buddha brain through trauma. Often cause physical pain.

Chakras: Energy centers associated with different areas of the body. 'Looks' like white or colored balls or sailing ship steering wheels.

Cellular brains: The self-aware organelles in the sperm, egg. or zygote cell that later develop into the multicelled brains of the fetus. Equivalent to saying 'organelle' or 'subcellular' brains.

Cellular memories: Memories of the sperm, egg, and zygote. Includes sensations, feelings, and thoughts. Also applied in the literature to memories of the body consciousness alone.

CoA - Center of Awareness: Using a finger, you can find your center of awareness by pointing at where 'you' are in your body. Can be at a particular point, or diffuse, and both internal to the body and external.

Copies: An experience of duplicating someone else's painful feelings or sensations in your own body. An alternative way to describe shamanic 'soul stealing'.

CPL - Calm, peace, lightness: The endpoint to healing a trauma, caused when the client goes into a peak state, usually temporarily.

Dowsing: Using pendulum or rod to communicate with the body consciousness. Same mechanism as in muscle testing or applied kinesiology.

DPR - Distant Personality Release: A technique to remove shell related material at the skin boundary on other people or on oneself.

EFT - Emotional Freedom Technique: A therapy that uses tapping on meridian points to eliminate emotional and physical discomfort. Classified as a power therapy, in the subcategory of an 'energy' or 'meridian' therapy.

False self: The self, experiencing the shell as dominating experience. Could also be called the personality. In deep inner exploration, can be experienced as a painful limitation or boundary at the skin by the self.

Felt sense: Labeled by Dr. Gendlin, it refers to a conscious awareness of how the body brain thinks and communicates.

Focusing: Invented by Dr. Gendlin, involves becoming aware of the body consciousness communicating (the 'felt sense') to release held traumatic material.

Fusion: The most connected that two or more brain awarenesses can get. When fused, they are one organism without any separate identity remaining. When all the brains fuse, their awareness can be seen to 'look' like a golden ball just below navel. Smaller and denser and feels more powerful than merged brains.

Gaia Instructions: All the steps in developmental events are directed by Gaia, and take into account current circumstances. The instructions for the steps can be translated into spoken language Also called 'Gaia commands'.

Generational trauma: Problems or beliefs passed down through the family line. Can be healed.

Heart: The limbic system, or old mammalian brain. Thinks in sequences of emotions, experiences itself in the center of the chest.

Holes: 'Look' like black holes in the body, feel like infinitely deep deficient emptiness. Encountered during some therapies. Caused by physical damage to the body.

Inner Peace state: A state of consciousness where a person's emotional past no longer feels traumatic. A subset of the Beauty Way state.

Kundalini: Characterized by the sensation of a small area of heat about the size of a silver dollar slowly moving up the spine. Can go on for months, and in some cases years. Stimulates traumas and other unusual 'spiritual' experiences into awareness, creating severe problems for most people.

Merging: Two or more people sharing awarenesses and memories. Feels like the person merging gets larger to include the other person. Can be dangerous, as 'soul stealing' can occur.

Merging of brains: The awarenesses of the biological brains can come together in various combinations. Fusion is a more extreme experience of merging.

Meridians: Energy channels that wind through the body. Used in therapies such as acupuncture and EFT.

Muscle testing: Communicating with the body consciousness by using muscle strength as an indicator. Same mechanism as applied kinesiology, and the terms are sometimes used interchangeably.

Mind: The neocortex, or primate brain. Thinks in thoughts, experiences itself in the head.

No-breath technique: Using breath or nose holding, will activate suppressed trauma around oxygen lack, especially during birth.

OBE (The out-of-body experience): Seeing without eyes separate from the physical body.

Past lives: Encountered in some therapies, the experience of having lived in the past or the future with a different body and personality.

Peak State: One of about 15 major states of consciousness that gives experiences and abilities that cannot be experienced in average consciousness. Felt as vast improvement to the average state. Can be had in combination and to various degrees. A number of sub states exist also.

Personality: The effect of a non-physical layer at the skin that gives one the sensation of having a skin boundary. Makes events and traumas feel 'personal'. Can be felt via chords by other people.

PTSD (Post Traumatic Stress Disorder): Category in the diagnostic manual for psychological problems, originated by Dr. Figley. Written for overt, major trauma, but symptoms occurs to lesser degree in small, apparently insignificant traumatic events.

Power therapy: Phrase coined by Dr. Figley, applied to extremely effective therapies that remove symptoms from post traumatic stress disorder and other issues.

Precellular trauma: Trauma that occurs to the biological system that is the prototype of the egg or sperm, before the egg or sperm have formed into a cell.

Psychological reversal: The individual has a counter commitment at the body consciousness level to healing or peak performance. In energy therapies, healing is blocked unless treated. In WHH, it causes the client not to want to heal, but does not block the healing directly.

Regenerative Healing: A particular type of physical healing occurring in just minutes. Range of healing includes injuries that cannot normally heal, such as scars, cut spines, etc. We formerly called it Radical Physical Healing (RPH).

Self: The part of us that experiences itself as 'I am'. It's eternal. The part of us that's in all of our past lives. Also called spirit. Also called the conscious awareness.

Self-identity: Each of the biological brains pretends it's someone or something else.

Shell: A layer right at skin level, composed of stuff related to what our spirit is made out of that gives us the sensation of having skin and keeps our awareness confined to our bodies. Can be experienced as burning or painful at the skin level.

Soul: Soul pieces or soul stealing or soul loss. Well described in Sandra Ingerman's Soul Retrieval. Involved with the underlying mechanism of schizophrenia.

Spirit: Same as self defined above.

Spiritual emergency: An experience usually classified as relating to spiritual or mystical traditions, experienced as traumatic or overwhelming to the level of being a crisis.

SUDS - Subjective units of distress scale: Used to evaluate the degree of pain in trauma. Originally from a scale of 1 to 10, common usage is now from 0 (no pain) to 10 (as much pain as it's possible to have).

TAT (Tapas Acupressure Technique): Invented by Tapas Fleming originally to heal allergies, also works on trauma and other issues. Recommended for generational trauma

Tetany: During breathwork, tetany is the experience of having part or all of the body feel paralyzed and/or with 'pins and needles'. It is due to trauma and is not a medical problem.

TFT (Thought Field Therapy): The original tapping on meridian therapy. Also discovered the phenomenon and a fix for 'psychological reversal'.

TIR (Traumatic Incident Reduction): A power therapy that uses regression.

Trauma: A moment in time, or string of moments where the sensations, emotions, and thoughts are stored. Causes difficulties for humans as they guide behavior inappropriately. Usually painful or difficult experiences. Trauma creates post traumatic stress disorder.

Trolling: Refers to looking for trauma in the past without first finding a symptom in the present.

Triune brain: The brain is built out of three separate biological brains, formed through evolution. They are the R-complex (body), the limbic system (heart), and the neocortex (mind). Each is self aware, built for different functions, and thinks by sensations, feelings, or thoughts.

Unconscious: The awarenesses (and actions) of the individual brains when the self is not merged with them. Also refers to the motivations the self has that are due to the shell trauma.

WHH (The Whole-Hearted Healing therapy): A regression technique. Uses the OBE experience to heal trauma.

Index

Printed in the United States
74433LV00001B/232

9 780973 468021